Government Issued
ZOMBIE
SURVIVAL HANDBOOK

Government Issued
ZOMBIE
SURVIVAL HANDBOOK

Everything You Need to Know to Survive the Outbreak

Gerald Kielpinski
Brian Gleisberg

Guffaw Press • Valencia, CA

Written and designed by
Gerald Kielpinski and Brian Gleisberg
Mantis Design, Inc.

Special thanks to Alley Getz for her wonderful talent
in Zombie creation.

Special thanks to Julie Luongo for her support and input.

Photo on page 32 © AlienCat/Fotolia; photo on page 66 © objectsforall/
Fotolia; photo on page 97 © Coka/Fotolia; photo on page 125 © Tootles/
Fotolia; photo on page 126 © Mila Gligoric/Fotolia; photo on page 136 ©
LeChatMachine/Fotolia; photo on page 190 © Michael Ransburg/Fotolia;
photo on page 194 © Marianne de Jong/Fotolia; photo on page 200 © dja65/
Fotolia; photo on page 201 © Robert Wilson/Fotolia; photo on page 203 (upper
left) © Tom Oliveira/Fotolia; photo on page 203 (lower right) © Parrus/Fotolia;
photo on page 217 © luSh/Fotolia; photo on page 237 © klikk/Fotolia; photo on
page 247 © LH/Fotolia

Published by
Guffaw Press
28377 Constellation Road
Valencia, CA 91355
www.guffawpress.com

ISBN: 978-1-55484-168-4

Printed in Canada.

ABOUT THE AUTHORS

Gerald Kielpinski recently transferred to the Bureau of Apocalyptic Events, Northeast Region, after spending the previous 10 years researching paranormal phenomena for an undisclosed corporation. He is known for his work in brainwave theory and reality-distortion science and has spent considerable time studying ancient cultures. Kielpinski's hobbies include spelunking, dungeon mastering, and surfing.

Brian Gleisberg has been a deep-cover field agent for the Bureau of Apocalyptic Events, Northeast Region, for the past 20 years. Some of his undercover occupations include the Department of Defense Police, poster magnate, welder, chemical operator, and laboratory technician. He played key roles in quelling the robot uprising of '95 and other still-classified apocalyptic phenomena.

Kielpinski and Gleisberg currently operate out of the greater Stroudsburg metropolitan area.

While every effort has been made to create a complete and accurate field guide, some inconsistencies, redundancies, and typographical errors may have occurred during the production of this book.

Always judge a situation by what you see on the ground.

Let common sense be your guide.

a slow hit is better than a fast miss

WHAT HAPPENED?

A pathogen known as the "Vrykolas-Romeros Virus" (VRV) began infecting humans throughout eastern Pennsylvania approximately six weeks prior to the printing of this book. VRV is unlike any virus humankind has ever seen before. It kills its host quickly and within moments reanimates the corpse as a "walking dead" creature that is compelled to bite humans and spread the virus. These abominations are herein referred to as "Zombies." Since the appearance of VRV, worldwide chaos has ensued. The power grid is down, supplies are finite, and Zombies are roaming the landscape. You have found yourself trying to survive as best as you can under these desperate circumstances. The government is determined to find a cure for the VRV, but until we do, you must adapt to overcome the daily challenges to survival. This book will help. Trust science.

Your government is working hard to find a cure for the VRV.

I-I A BRIEF HISTORY

At the time of this writing, it has been 41 days since VRV was first discovered—a day commonly referred to as "Z-Day." At this point, VRV is known to have spread throughout the world. The "Carrier nature" is responsible for dramatically increasing the spread of VRV. Carriers are people who have been infected with VRV but do not develop Zombie traits. Carriers can spread VRV through the transfer of bodily fluids. To make matters worse, Carriers are often unaware of their condition. This has resulted in Carriers unwittingly spreading VRV.

It is imperative that an understanding of the Carrier nature be disseminated to all survivors.

Your government is currently headquartered in an underground facility. Our top scientists are hard at work. Test subjects are easy to find. Either a cure will be found, or Zombies will be eliminated.

See **CHAPTER 2: CARRIER NATURE.**

The act of kissing can transmit the VRV from unknowing Carriers.

WHAT HAPPENED?

I–II THE WILL TO LIVE

Nothing is more important to your survival than your will to live. The will to live is demonstrated by never giving up. Humankind has overcome many desperate circumstances in the past and will again. We can generate strength from the following:

- Responsibility to family and friends
- Respect for the dead or fallen
- Desire to lead loved ones (or humanity as a whole) to a better future.
- Faith in religion

I–III KNOWLEDGE: YOUR GREATEST ASSET

An open mind and a willingness to learn will help you survive, even thrive, in this challenging environment.

LEARN FROM THIS BOOK

Read and re-read this book. Teach skills you have learned to others. The act of teaching will ground the skill in you.

LEARN DIRECTLY FROM OTHERS

Compare your experiences with those of other survivors. Look for commonalities that confirm trends, and examine differences. Share any skills you have, and encourage others to share the skills they have, as well. Some people are receptive to learning from others–especially if it involves thwarting or eliminating Zombies. Some are not receptive. Do not try to force your views on those who are unreceptive.

WHAT HAPPENED?

LEARN BY OBSERVATION
Study Zombies and note their behaviors. Observe how people react to this new environment, and emulate what works for them.

I–IV ADAPTATION
The information provided in this book lays a foundation for your survival, but nothing can prepare you for every situation that may occur on any given day. It is important that you are able to adapt to unique conditions and learn from your mistakes. Do your best not to dwell on mistakes; do your best to learn from whatever lessons you can and move on. Visualize how you will make better decisions in the future based on your past experiences. Do not allow yourself to be overwhelmed by guilt and regret. Learn to focus on the present moment.

I–V OVERCOMING STRESS/PANIC ATTACKS
STRESS
Mental fatigue can be treated to some degree by talking about your experiences and maintaining a routine. Training, exercising, and maintaining your equipment will help alleviate some symptoms. Allow time between demanding or intense missions, if possible. Attempt to get regular sleep, drink plenty of fluids, and eat normal portions of food. Keep up your personal hygiene if enough water is available. Talk about your worries and fears; bottled up emotions can manifest themselves in unwanted ways at inopportune times.

WHAT HAPPENED?

PANIC ATTACKS

Panic can strike anyone. If a member of your group becomes panic stricken or hysterical, you must take action. If you are traveling where Zombie contact is probable, you might consider taking a temporary defensive position to devote some time to calming your party members. Calm panic stricken or overstressed comrades with the following techniques:

- Project confidence and decisiveness.
- Speak softly.
- Remind them of their importance to the team.
- Do not make promises that you cannot keep.
- Administer warm food and drink.
- Take as much time as is tactically feasible.

If a team member is hysterical, not responding to reason, and jeopardizing the safety of others, he or she may need to be gagged to avoid attracting Zombies. Duct tape is easy to use and reliable.

See **CHAPTER 12: SURVIVAL HABITS** for more information on maintaining a healthy routine.

I–VI GROUP DYNAMICS

Finding other survivors and working together will dramatically increase your chances of survival. The optimum size of a survival group is three to five people. Groups larger than five are generally less safe because (1) they are easier for Zombies to find, and (2) they are harder to manage efficiently. The ability to make quick decisions and successfully execute them is what gives a survival group its strength. If your group has more than five people and is not acting efficiently, it may be wise to split up into smaller groups. Familial Survival Groups (FSGs) have been reported to work well and usually have a predesignated leader.

Survival groups must act in a democratic way, allowing each person to have a voice. However, there must also be a leader—one person who can be trusted to make smart, well-informed decisions for the entire group. This person can be a man or woman.

See **CHAPTER 14: TEAMWORK** for more information on choosing a leader and functioning as a cohesive unit.

Summary

With the knowledge presented in this handbook—plus the ability to adapt to unique situations and learn from mistakes—a strong group of survivors who are unified in a common purpose should be able to thrive during the current crisis.

This is a team of exerienced Zombie hunters It is possible to go on the offensive and hasten the eradication of the Zombie menace if you know how to work together.

[Photo courtesy "South Stroud Kill Klub"]

PART I

SURVIVAL

AT HOME

CHAPTER 1
THE VIRUS

The VRV is transmitted by infected blood and any other bodily fluid—most frequently through the bite of a Zombie. If a Zombie bites you and breaks the skin, you have approximately 90 seconds to diagnose yourself. If you begin to sweat profusely, feel nauseous, and shake uncontrollably, you have been infected and will soon become a Zombie. If you are bitten and do not go through these stages, you are most likely a Carrier of the disease.

1–1 IF YOU FEEL NAUSEOUS
You are infected. Approximately 90 seconds after infection you will regurgitate a large amount of blood and die. Survivors should stay clear of any infected victims until after the victim has vomited and died.

1–2 DEATH TO REANIMATION INTERVAL
Victims of VRV will remain deceased for a brief time before reanimating as a Zombie. The more body mass, the longer it will take, but a good general rule of thumb is one minute. If it takes longer, consider that bonus time.

Body Type	Approx. Time Until Reanimation
Infant	45 seconds
Child	1 minute
Adolescent/Teen	1 minute
Adult (thin)	1 minute
Adult (average)	90 seconds
Adult (overweight)	2 or more minutes

A saw can be used to sever the head of a fallen teammate.

If the remaining survivors have the proper tools or weapons, adequate time, and enough will, they should immediately sever the corpse's head or completely destroy its brain to prevent the corpse from reanimating into a Zombie. Children and sensitive survivors should not be allowed to witness this difficult (and often gruesome) act. This is the reality you live in; do your best to accept it.

1-3 REANIMATION

If the corpse's head is not severed or its brain is not destroyed, the virus will take control of the body and reanimate it. The eyes of the host will open, and the body will "jump to life." At this stage, the host is considered to be a Zombie. Zombies are not human beings and should not be treated as such.

1-4 SUICIDE & CONSENSUAL RE-KILLING

The act of suicide in response to being bitten is a viable and noble option. This reduces the number of Zombies and eliminates the psychological trauma of having a loved one or friend encounter you as a lethal threat. If you are incapable of taking your own life, a designated team member can perform this service for you and society.

Consider the following:

• Live with an eye toward this possible outcome, leaving nothing unsaid. Do not wait until you are faced with suicide to tell loved ones how you feel about them. You might not have time to do it later.

• Suicides and consensual re-killings are best performed with a firearm. Most other methods are either not effective or take too long.

• If an impact or bladed weapon must be used, wait until the victim has died before destroying the brain or severing the spine.

• Whenever possible, the act of suicide should be conducted away from children and loved ones.

• When suicide or consensual re-killing is not possible, the person who has been bitten should run as far away from the group as possible before dying and reanimating.

1–5 RIGOR MORTIS

Immediately following reanimation, a Zombie is in its most dangerous phase because the effects of rigor mortis have not yet begun. Currently Zombies are known to have three distinct stages of development: Fresh, Rigored, and PMZ.

STAGE 1: FRESH ZOMBIE (3 HOURS)

The speed and agility of a "fresh" Zombie are equal to those of a normal human being. Rigor mortis, a stiffening of the muscles, usually starts to take place approximately three hours after reanimation.

STAGE 2: RIGORED ZOMBIE (3 DAYS)

Zombies experiencing rigor mortis move with a very "jerky" gait. Their legs stiffen, and they struggle against it. At full rigor, a Zombie may be writhing on the ground, but it will still have the ability to bite effectively.

Full rigor occurs approximately 12 hours after the initial reanimation. Rigor mortis dissipates over a period of approximately three days, at which point decomposition begins.

STAGE 3: PMZ (INDEFINITELY)

When rigor mortis has fully resolved, a Zombie will be able to move and run again but not as fast as a fresh Zombie. This condition is known as a Post Mortis Zombie, or PMZ. PMZs walk or run awkwardly, depending on the condition of the host prior to infection. It should be noted that a Zombie's blood at this stage has coagulated and therefore has a highly decreased "splatter effect."

Limbs can be removed from Zombies with no effect on their motivation or animation. Government tests have confirmed this trait. Even with its legs removed, a Zombie will use its arms to crawl toward potential victims with gusto.

With the passage of time, it can be surmised that decomposition will impair a Zombie's coordination and overall ability to walk to the point of total uselessness. Time is on your side.

VIRAL/FUNGAL COMORBIDITY

There have been scattered reports of Zombies that do not decompose due to the presence of a previously unknown fungus that retards decomposition. This symbiotic relationship could represent a new type of Zombie. At the time of printing, this effect has not been verified.

1–6 ZOMBIE TRAITS

• **Interested in Humans**
Zombies are interested in one thing: biting humans. All other animals, including cats, dogs, and horses are not recognized by Zombies.

• **Single Minded**
Zombies usually take a direct path toward human targets. If something blocks that path, Zombies will generally beat on or claw at the obstacle rather than look for an alternate route.

• **Do Not Feel Pain**

• **Never Sleep**

• **Sensitive to Light**
Zombies prefer dark places and are more active at night. This is attributed to their slight sensitivity to light. Zombies reportedly have been blinded by powerful bright lights.

• Attracted to Shopping Malls

At present, there is no understanding of Zombies' apparent attraction to retail outlets, shopping malls, and discount warehouses.

• Prone to Feeding Frenzies

Zombies have been observed not only biting humans but also eating human flesh. There are reports of Zombies gnawing off entire limbs in the initial attack. While in a feeding frenzy, Zombies are focused and unwavering.

• Attracted to Feeding Frenzies

Zombies have been observed joining other Zombies in feeding frenzies and forming very dangerous hordes.

• Drawn to Hot Dogs, Bacon, and Sausage

Zombies are irresistibly attracted to the scent of hot dogs, bacon, sausage and other packaged meat products.

• Tend to Moan

Zombies have been reported to make many noises that can be best described as a kind of moan. Some are more "talkative" than others. Some never stop "talking."

• Attracted to Human-Related Movement and Sounds

Zombies are attracted to anything that is distinctly human, including unnatural light.

• Attack Human Representations

Zombies have been reported to attack mannequins, pictures of humans, and even recordings of humans talking or rapping.

• No Heat Signature
Zombies do not produce heat, unless they are set on fire.

• Do Not Dance
Zombies do not dance or recognize music as anything other than noise, but they may investigate it.

• Incapable of Smiling
Zombies never smile or express emotions.

• Can Walk Underwater
Zombies do not breathe and have been known to walk underwater through lakes and very slow-moving rivers. Deep waterways with significant currents are effective natural barriers.

• Will Freeze Solid
Zombies will freeze when temperatures drop below 32°F. If the temperature rises, however, a frozen Zombie will thaw and operate normally.

• Show Slight Variances in Behaviors
Zombie behaviors vary slightly from Zombie to Zombie. For example, some may moan, some may not, and some are more easily distracted than others.

1–7 ZOMBIE HORDES
Zombies can form hordes. Initially there must be a powerful attraction. There are currently three known causes of horde formation:

CHAPTER 1
THE VIRUS

1. FEEDING FRENZIES

Zombies come together when feeding on human body parts. In this conflagration, Zombie hordes have been reported to form.

2. MUTUALLY SHARED HUMAN TARGET

There have been limited reports of Zombie hordes forming when Zombies are stacked together when driving toward a visible human target. One report reportedly occurred when Zombies were attracted to a movie poster featuring Leonardo DiCaprio inside a barricaded room.

3. RIGORED ZOMBIES

Zombies going through acute rigor mortis can attract other Zombies. Although hordes have been observed to form in this way, the accounts are rare.

NOTE: Simple distractions do not generally form hordes.

• Self Propagation

Hordes have been reported to be self propagating, absorbing other Zombies as they move.

• Horde Mentality

Hordes occur when Zombies within close proximity stop acting independently and begin acting cohesively. Hordes adopt a "hive mind" and, as such, tend to have vision in all directions. If a target is spotted, the entire horde will attack as one unit.

Consider the following:

CHAPTER 1
THE VIRUS

Zombie hordes have been reported to break down barricades and overcome large obstacles.

There have been reports of a 100+ Zombie "mega-horde" nicknamed "Anna." Mega-hordes should be avoided. The government will target mega-hordes to restore order. Science will prevail.

It is in your best interest to eliminate Zombies if you have the means.

See **CHAPTER 20: ZOMBIE HUNTING** for more information on Zombie-elimination techniques.

1–8 SIGNS THAT SOMEONE IS NOT A ZOMBIE

• Signaling That You Are Human
Always walk upright and show good posture. To signal visually, move your arms in an organized deliberate manner back and forth and smile. To signal with sound, use a whistle or speak clearly to indicate you are human.

• Determining if Someone Is a Zombie
If you are trying to determine if someone is a Zombie, err on the side of caution.

Summary

Understanding the nature of Zombies will give you an advantage over them. Study them and take notes. Compare your notes with the observations of other survivors.

Zombies are interested in humans. These mannequins attracted the attention of a Zombie that attacked them continuously for several days.

[Photo courtesy Erick Ingersoll]

Zombies feel no pain and are not slowed down by most injuries. This Zombie was bludgeoned with a bat and still was not impeded from spreading the disease.

[Photo found in camera]

Zombies are known to engage in feeding frenzies in which they gnaw off entire limbs of the recently deceased. This Zombie was so caught up in its feeding frenzy that it completely ignored the photographer.

[Photo courtesy "Charlie from Sciota"]

Zombies demonstrate slight variances in behavior. They can be unpredictable. This feeding Zombie reportedly dropped its meal in order to chase the photographer. In other cases, Zombies have been observed to be so engrossed in a feeding frenzy that they ignored human targets.

[Photo courtesy of James Dennis]

Zombies do not produce body heat and will therefore freeze solid. This Zombie was frozen at the time of shooting, allowing survivors to approach safely. Frozen Zombies are best re-killed using a bow saw or axe to sever their heads while they are frozen. If allowed to thaw, Zombies will regain mobility.

[Photo courtesy "B-Town Boys"]

30

do not rely on
rumors & speculation

CHAPTER 2

CARRIER NATURE

Carriers of the VRV are both a liability and an asset. They are dangerous because they can intentionally or unintentionally spread the virus with a bite or a kiss. But because they are immune to VRV, they can help combat Zombies without fear of being infected. It is essential that Carriers learn about themselves as quickly as possible. Despite their potential for spreading the disease, educated Carriers can be highly beneficial to your survival group, and may hold the key to solving this crisis.

2–1 CARRIER PHYSIOLOGY

Carriers undergo both a physical and mental transformation when the VRV enters their bloodstream, but it might take up to a week before all side effects become apparent. Although the side effects may affect their mood and behavior, Carriers are still fully functioning human beings—they are still the same person they were before they were bitten. Carriers should be treated differently based on current circumstances. As a general rule, Carriers should be shown the same respect as any other human being. Carriers have been reported experiencing the following side effects:

- Sensitivity to sunlight. (Sunglasses are an effective way to solve this problem.)
- Reduced body temperature. A Carrier's body temperature may drop to as low as 94°F.
- An unhealthy, pale appearance. Carriers operate effectively in this state and should not be considered sick, even though they might appear to have an illness.

Human beings are social creatures and have a need for interpersonal relationships. It is natural for Carriers to seek one another other out.

2–2 CARRIER CONSIDERATIONS

Carriers are inherently armed with a deadly weapon and should be watched closely. If they become erratic or aggressive, consider assigning them to separate quarters for a time. Carriers should be locked in separate rooms when sleeping. If a Carrier threatens to bite you or anyone in your group, consider any possible means of self defense. If a Carrier is injured and bleeds, treat the wound with caution, wearing protective gloves and a face mask. Carriers should not be appointed the leader of a group.

2–3 CARRIER RESPONSIBILITY

Carriers must prevent their bodily fluids from contacting anyone or anything. They must not kiss or engage in sexual intercourse or oral sex with anyone except other Carriers. They must not sneeze or cough on anyone. Responsible Carriers wear an item that shields their nose and mouth at all times.

2–4 CARRIER ADVANTAGES

Many lives have reportedly been saved by Carriers' ability to engage in close combat with Zombies without fear of being infected. Because Carriers are immune to the VRV, they are suited to undertake certain dangerous missions.

- Send Carriers to retrieve supplies in low-risk danger zones.
- Use Carriers to run reconnaissance when planning missions.
- Position a Carrier as a point-person or scout on missions.

Although Carriers are immune to the effects of the VRV, they will still be attacked by Zombies and are therefore at risk of ordinary infections or injuries from bites. There have been reports of Carriers being overwhelmed by Zombies.

Summary

Carriers are human beings and entitled to basic human rights. However, because they are inherently dangerous, certain exceptions must be made. It is the responsibility of a Carrier to wear proper clothing, and it is within the right of survivors to banish a Carrier to isolation if they are behaving erratically or extremely moody. Carriers are very valuable for executing missions and may also hold the key to a cure. Spread this information about Carriers to everyone you encounter.

show good posture

The VRV resides in the brain of its host and extends through the nervous system to control the motor functions of the host body. Destroy the brain or sever the spine at the base of the skull to destroy a Zombie. Approximately 25 to 30 percent of the brain matter needs to be depleted for effective elimination. Some basic knowledge of the brain and the skull will improve your ability to eradicate the Zombie menace.

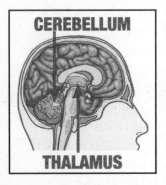

The VRV needs the brain to function

3–1 THE BRAIN

The brain is the only part of the target you should be concerned with obliterating, as it is believed to be the only organ that harbors the "Zombie virus" (VRV). The exact mechanism of control is not known, nor is it within the scope of this manual to hypothesize on the science behind this outbreak.

Direct damage to the thalamus or cerebellum has proven to be extremely effective regardless of the amount of damage inflicted to the rest of the brain. However, destroying 25 to 30 percent of the brain matter is a good rule of thumb for effective Zombie eradication.

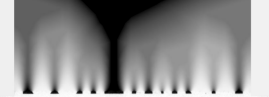

As a tactic for the seasoned Zombie hunter, specifically attacking the thalamus and cerebellum may help save ammunition and conserve energy. However, as a tactic for the novice Zombie eliminator, targeting specific areas of the brain is not advisable because these parts are relatively small, located deep in the skull, and surrounded by large amounts of brain tissue. It it recommended that novices simply try to destroy as much of the brain as possible.

Regardless of tactic, the destruction of brain matter is crucial for eliminating a Zombie. Do not stop smashing the skull until the target stops moving. When the Zombie is effectively eliminated, it will slump and go limp. As you gain experience, it will be easier to determine how much destruction is enough; but until then "over-kill" is the general rule, unless in a horde situation.

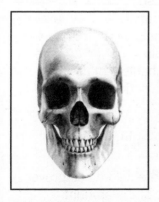

The skull can be compromised with direct strikes.

3–2 THE SKULL

Technically, "skull" refers to the complete unit of the cranium, brain case, and mandible (structure of the jaw). For brevity, the term "skull" will be used herein in lieu of "cranium."

The average thickness of a man's skull is 6.5 mm, whereas a woman's is 7.1 mm. The inside of the skull is reinforced with ridges, the most prominent running from front to back along the top portion of the skull. The portions of the skull directly to the front and rear tend to be thicker and more resistant to destruction. The front of the skull contains the sinuses, which may cushion an impact and protect the brain. As a rule, the "corners" of the skull are the most vulnerable areas. When using impact weapons, such as a baseball bat or tire iron, it is crucial to smash the skull as directly as possible; hitting the skull on the side may only have a glancing effect.

The eye sockets provide a pathway to the deep brain and can be targets for pointed weapons. However, it is difficult to hit a moving eye socket with any weapon. When a Zombie is pinned (at a fence or barricade) or held (using a yoke), it is more susceptible to pointed weapons. For simplicity, the act of Zombie elimination by means of employing a pointed weapon against the eye socket is called "staking," and weaponry associated with the technique are called "stake weapons."

Projectile weapons, including firearms and bows, should be employed against the sides of the skull or into the eye sockets. The skull is capable of deflecting projectiles that target the skull from extreme oblique angles. Your bullet or arrow should impact the skull as perpendicular as possible. Experienced marksmen with weapons of sufficient power are able to target nearly any portion of the skull. Let common sense be your guide.

3–3 THE SPINE
Severing the spine anywhere between the first and third cervical vertebrae will eliminate a Zombie. Severing the

spine below the third cervical vertebrae may create a Zombie that is immobile yet still able to bite and infect humans. Severing the spine requires skill, strength, and a suitable weapon. It is not recommended for the novice Zombie hunter.

3–4 COOKING THE BRAIN

The brain can be effectively destroyed by fire, but the process is lengthy. A good rule of thumb for effective brain frying is one hour from the point at which the Zombie becomes totally consumed by fire. Burning as a method of Zombie eradication should be employed only by seasoned Zombie killers.

Summary

The only way to eliminate a Zombie and put an end to this plague is to destroy the Zombie brain. You must destroy at least 25 to 30 percent of the brain to be effective. Overkill is the rule of thumb. The skull is best attacked with direct strikes, but the eye sockets may be exploited in certain situations. Severing the spine is a different and effective way to eliminate a Zombie. Firearms are the best weapon to use against Zombies, but they will also draw the attention of other Zombies. The thalamus and cerebellum should be targeted if possible.

Aim for the head or legs. This Zombie was shot multiple times in the chest and did not stop. Zombies can only be re-killed if the brain is at least partially destroyed. Zombies can be slowed down significantly if their legs are destroyed.

[Photo courtesy "86 Rangers"]

Target the eye sockets because they are an effective path to the brain. They are not easy to hit, but can be punctured by a variety of household objects, including screwdrivers, ski poles with the baskets removed, or stakes carved out of wood from chairs and furniture. Spears can be made from broom and mop handles.

emotional intelligence is a survival trait

Pistols, rifles, and shotguns are the best defense against Zombies. Their sheer destructive power cannot be ignored. Yet the harnessed power that makes firearms so effective also makes them a potential hazard. The sound created by a gunshot will draw Zombies to your location from miles away. Always bear this in mind when deciding whether to use a firearm in any given situation.

4–1 GUN SAFETY

Those who disregard gun saftey rules should be corrected or avoided as they may be greater threats than Zombies.

Proper gun handling includes the following points:

- Treat every firearm as if it is loaded, charged, and ready to fire.
- Always keep the muzzle of a firearm pointed in a safe direction.
- Keep your finger off of the trigger until your sights are on target. Do not rely on the safety; it is a mechanical device and, as such, capable of failure.
- Identify your target and know what lays beyond it.

FIREARM M1911

The M1911 pistol is chambered for the .45 ACP, known for its stopping power. It is perhaps the most successful combat pistol ever designed. Its ease of use and proven reliability make it ideal for Zombie eradication.

4–2 PISTOLS

Pistols are limited to engagement distances of 25 yards or less, although proficient shooters may be capable of greater ranges. As a rule, pistols use less powerful cartridges. Pistols are not a good choice for the long-distance elimination of Zombies. Pistols shine in close-quarter combat where its compact nature allows you to employ it to its best effect. Pistols should be carried in you hand, in a holster, or in a pack. Do not carry pistols in your waistband or pocket! There are two basic types of pistols: revolvers and semi-automatics.

REVOLVERS

Revolvers are identified by the presence of a cylinder and can be further divided into two groups: double action and single action. Double-action revolvers utilize the action of squeezing the trigger to both draw the hammer back and revolve the cylinder into battery. Single-action revolvers utilize the action of manually cocking the hammer to revolve the cylinder into battery. You are required to cock the hammer each time you wish to fire. Generally the cylinder is unlocked by pressing a latch on the left side of the frame near your thumb. This will allow the cylinder to swing out so the chambers can be loaded or empty cases removed. Single-

action revolvers usually have a loading gate at the rear of the cylinder that must swung out to expose the chambers individually for reloading and unloading. Spent cases are ejected by the use of a plunger (called the "ejector rod") at the front of the cylinder. The cylinder is closed by pressing it back into position in the frame of the pistol. Generally there is no manually operated safety on a revolver.

SEMI-AUTOMATIC PISTOLS

Semi-automatic pistols are identified by a magazine found within the handle. Attempt to find the safety and engage it. It will be located on the left side of the pistol, positioned such that you could operate it with your thumb if you grasped the pistol with your right hand. Look for a serrated or textured lever or switch and either a letter "S" or "F" or red and white dots. Move the safety so that either the "S" or white dot is revealed. (The 1911 family of pistols has no markings; the lever simply swings up to engage a notch on the slide.) There are many "safe action" pistols that have no manual safety, and if after some examination you do not discover a safety, you may have encountered one of these. (Note: Some pistols have a de-cocker mechanism either built into the safety or as a separate control. If you engage the safety with the pistol cocked and the hammer releases or if you hear a click, it is likely you have one.)

CHAPTER 4
FIREARMS

To unload a semi-automatic pistol, you must remove the magazine (often referred to as the "clip"). Look for a button or lever where the trigger guard (the loop of metal or plastic that surrounds the trigger) joins the grip. On some pistols, the magazine release is located on the bottom of the handle. Work this button or lever until the magazine slides out of the butt (handle) of the weapon and set it aside. To clear the weapon, hold the pistol with one hand on the grip, without putting a finger on the trigger, and the other hand holding the top, where the barrel is located. Vigorously pull the top part (the "slide") toward the rear. (The 1911 family of pistols will require the safety to be in the "fire" position to accomplish this.) This will eject any chambered cartridge. Hold the slide to the rear and inspect the chamber (the rear of the barrel). If there is no cartridge in the chamber, the weapon is cleared.

The magazine is loaded by pressing rounds down and to the rear beneath the feed lips of the magazine. To ready the pistol for use, insert the magazine into the pistol until it clicks. Press the slide release to allow the slide to slam forward into battery. The slide release is generally located on the left side of the weapon above the trigger. Engage the safety if present. The weapon is now loaded and ready to fire. Practice unloading and reloading until you can do it efficiently under any circumstance.

4–3 SHOTGUNS

Shotguns offer devastating firepower at close range. Their employment is limited to shorter ranges as by-product of shotgun ballistics. Shot-shells, except slugs, discharge

FIREARM MOSSBERG 500

Mossberg 500 series shotguns provide reliability and durability under harsh conditions. You will find them everywhere. They will tolerate heavy use and less-than-ideal ammunition.

many small pellets. As the range increases, these small pellets lose energy to the point that they may not be able to penetrate the skull. In the case of buckshot, which utilizes fewer but larger pellets, the pattern of the shot may open up to the point where effective hits are difficult to achieve. Shotguns generally lack a sight except for a small bead near the muzzle because shotguns are designed to be pointed, not aimed. Use shotguns in close-quarter combat and for clearing buildings of the Zombie threat. There are three main types of shotguns: break action, pump action, and semi automatic. Shotgun shells are available in different gauges and lengths. Use only shells of the correct gauge. Use only shells shorter than the chamber of your weapon. The barrel will be marked as to the gauge and length of the chamber.

BREAK-ACTION SHOTGUNS
Break-action shotguns take time to reload and, in a combat situation, are only capable of eliminating as many Zombies as the number of barrels they have—either one or two. They tend to be unwieldy. The Federal Firearms Regulations that govern the length of firearm barrels have been suspended during this crisis, allowing you to legally saw the barrels of these weapons down to a more manageable size.

To clear a break-action shotgun, find the lever or button that allows the action to open. Single-barrel guns generally have a release button on the right side of the hammer. Double-barrel guns have a lever on top and to the rear of the receiver that is swung to either side to break the action. Open the action, revealing the chambers. Ensure they are empty.

To load a break-action shotgun, insert a shotgun shell of the correct gauge into each empty chamber and close the action and engage the safety, if present. Some newer model double-barrel shotguns have an automatic safety that engages when the action is closed. The safety is disengaged with a sliding button on the tang (the metal strip behind the receiver).

Double-barreled break-action shotguns will have either two triggers (each firing one barrel) or a single trigger that operates both barrels. One squeeze will fire the first barrel, another will fire the second.

PUMP-ACTION SHOTGUNS

Pump-action shotguns are desirable because of their relative insensitivity to ammunition of less-than-ideal type or condition. Pump-action types will generally feed, fire, and eject a wider of variety of ammunition than semi-automatic types. The safety is typically located on top and to the rear of the receiver, should be reachable with your thumb.

To clear a pump-action shotgun, engage the safety and locate the slide release button to the rear of the trigger guard. Depress the slide release button and vigorously slide the fore end to the rear. Repeat this until all ammunition has been ejected from the weapon and the chamber is empty.

To load a pump-action shotgun, engage the safety and insert shells into the magazine tube through the rectangular hole in the bottom of the receiver. Push each shell forward into the magazine tube until it catches. Repeat until the magazine will no longer accept shells.

Pump shotguns can be "topped off" by inserting ammunition into the magazine when time and tactics permit.

Some pump-action and automatic hunting shotguns will have their magazine limited to two or three shells with a plug. This plug is usually a wood or plastic rod inserted into the tubular magazine. It can be removed to allow the maximum amount of capacity.

SEMI-AUTOMATIC SHOTGUNS

To clear an automatic shotgun of shells, engage the safety and grasp the charging handle on the right side of the shotgun and pull to the rear. Continue to do this until both the magazine and chamber are empty.

FIREARM SAIGA 12

The Saiga-12 is a Kalashnikov pattern 12-gauge combat shotgun. It has a removable box magazine. The tested and proven loose construction in the AK style results in high reliability, a prized trait in semi-automatic shotguns.

Automatic shotguns are loaded in the same way as pump-action shotguns. Shells are pushed through the loading port under the receiver, forward into the tubular magazine.

To charge an automatic shotgun, load the magazine and pull the charging handle to the rear and let go. Do not "ride" the handle forward. Automatic shotguns can be topped off at any time by inserting shells into the magazine.

As a rule, automatic shotguns are less forgiving of dirt and less-than-ideal ammunition.

4–4 RIFLES

Rifles are most effective at long ranges at which their accuracy and power can be brought to bear in relative safety. They can be unwieldy in close situations, but carbine-length weapons can be useful in tight spots. Rifles come in four types: lever action, bolt action, pump action and semi automatic.

LEVER-ACTION RIFLES

Lever-action rifles are reminiscent of the classic "cowboy rifle." They are reliable and easy to operate. A lever in the vicinity of the trigger works the action. Simply swing

FIREARM **MARLIN MODEL 336**

Most commonly chambered in .30-30 Winchester or .35 Remington, the Marlin Model 336 has a flat top receiver allowing optical sights over traditional iron sights. It is accurate, easily maintained, and built for longevity.

the lever all the way forward and return it in one vigorous motion. To clear the weapon, swing the lever forward and observe the chamber through the ejection port, which is the oblong hole where spent cases are ejected.

Loading the magazine is accomplished via a loading gate, usually located on the right-hand side of the weapon. There will be a scalloped, spring-loaded gate covering the opening. Insert ammunition of the correct type, bullet end first, into this opening. Slide the round toward the front until the gate catches it. Repeat this process until the magazine is full. Some bolt-action, .22 rifles will have a tubular magazine with a knurled knob near the muzzle. Generally this knob is rotated a quarter-turn and slid out far enough to allow ammunition to pass through a cartridge-shaped slot on the magazine tube.

Older lever-action rifles may not have a conventional safety; instead, they have a "half-cock" safety, which is engaged by carefully holding the hammer and simultaneously pulling the trigger. Once the hammer is free, release the trigger and allow the hammer to stop halfway between full cock and all the way down. This may be difficult, so a good practice is to carry the rifle with the magazine loaded but the chamber empty. Charge the weapon upon Zombie contact.

An advantage to this type of rifle is that you can feed ammunition into it at any time, whereas clip-fed firearms are generally reloaded only when empty.

BOLT-ACTION RIFLES

Bolt-action rifles are the most common type of rifle you will encounter. They are reliable and have the potential for the greatest accuracy. They are operated by manipulating the bolt handle, which can be found on the right-hand side of the weapon to the rear of the receiver. The action is cycled by lifting the bolt handle up until it stops and pulling the bolt to the rear until it stops. Then the bolt is pushed forward until it stops and the handle is pushed down until it stops. This series of events should occur as one vigorous motion. To clear a bolt-action rifle, pull the bolt to the rear and observe the chamber through the ejection port.

There are two common methods of loading a bolt-action rifle: through the ejection port and with a detachable magazine. Occasionally you will encounter a single-shot bolt-action, which accepts only one round at a time. To load through the ejection port, press a round down on the spring-loaded follower at the bottom of the ejection port until it is captured by the feed lips. Repeat until it will not accept any more rounds. To load a detachable magazine, remove the magazine from the rifle and press rounds back and down under the feed lips. Ensure the rounds are fully seated to the rear of the magazine. When you insert the magazine into the rifle, ensure the rounds are pointed the correct direction (toward the open chamber).

PUMP-ACTION RIFLES

You may come across a pump-action rifle, which could be mistaken for a pump-action shotgun. Pump-action rifles operate similarly to pump-action shotguns.

FIREARM AR-15

AR-15 rifles are highly configurable and customizable. Their ease of use and accuracy are legendary. They use the common 5.56x45 mm NATO rifle cartridge and can be fitted with laser pointers that literally draw Zombies into view.

SEMI-AUTOMATIC RIFLES

Semi-automatic rifles encompass the widest variety of operational controls, safeties, and magazines. To clear and make safe a semi-automatic rifle, pull the charging handle or cocking knob to the rear and observe the chamber to ensure it is empty. On the M16/AR15 family of rifles, there is a T-shaped handle below the rear sight. (On most other rifles, the cocking knob is located on the right-hand side.) To chamber a round, insert a fresh magazine or ensure the integral magazine is loaded, and pull the cocking knob or charging handle to the rear and release it. Do not "ride" the handle forward; pull and release it. This allows the bolt to strip a fresh round and insert it into the chamber. Engage the safety.

To load a detachable magazine, remove the magazine from the rifle and press rounds back and down under the feed lips. Ensure the rounds are fully seated to the rear of the magazine by firmly tapping the magazine against your palm. Some semi-automatic rifles, particularly hunting rifles, have tubular magazines with various means of loading. Some semi-automatic .22 rifles will have a tubular magazine with a knurled knob near the muzzle. Generally this knob is rotated a quarter-turn and slid out far enough to allow ammunition to pass through a cartridge-shaped slot on the magazine tube.

The location of the safety varies with the type of rifle. Usually military rifles have the safety in the form of a switch or lever in the vicinity of your right thumb. An exception is the Kalashnikov family of rifles on which the safety is a pressed-sheet-metal slide that also functions as a dust cover for the ejection port. Semi-automatic hunting rifles generally have a safety operated by your right thumb near the top and rear of the receiver or operated by you trigger finger near the trigger guard.

THE .22 LONG RIFLE

It is easy to dismiss the .22 for its limited power, but that would be a grave error. While it is true that the .22 is not an effective long-range Zombie eliminating cartridge, it can be very effective at close range. The .22 round is indeed very effective at destroying brain matter at close range. Ammo is light and widely available. A .22 is also an excellent hunting tool and will keep your stew pot full if you do your part. Squirrels, rabbits, feral dogs and cats, groundhogs, and even deer will fall before the .22.

4–5 AMMUNITION

Firearms will be marked with the type of ammunition required; simply match the markings on the weapon with the markings on the box of ammunition or the round itself. There is very little interchangeability. The most common exceptions are using .38 special ammunition in weapons chambered for .357 Magnum or using .223 in weapons chambered for 5.56 NATO.

This diagram represents your sight picture. Everything in black is the rear sight. The red and white is your forward sight, and the grey is a Zombie approaching.

4–6 MARKSMANSHIP

It is beyond the scope of this manual to present a comprehensive treatise on all forms of marksmanship. This section provides novice and intermediate marksmen with some fundamentals to enhance their abilities. Experienced marksmen and hunters may disregard some of the basic instruction offered here but should review sections on the use of Zombie-specific techniques. Well trained, safe shooters should assist beginners whenever possible. The respect of and skill with firearms will hasten a Zombie-free future.

• **Sight picture** is a term that refers to the correct alignment of the sights relative to the target.

• **Trigger control** refers to the manipulation required to squeeze the trigger to the point where the firearm discharges without causing the sight alignment to be compromised. As a rule, you should engage the trigger with the pad of your index finger between the tip and first joint. Care must be exercised to squeeze the trigger directly to the rear, increasing pressure when the sights are in correct relation to the target and holding pressure as the sights drift out of alignment. Despite the apparent simplicity, this process takes time to master.

• **Breath control** refers to the technique of working with your natural pattern of breathing rather than against it. There are two schools of thought on this; select one technique that works for you. Some shooters advocate taking a breath, exhaling half of it, and holding. From this point you have a few seconds to squeeze the trigger before the lack of oxygen compromises your ability to shoot accurately. Others advocate "respiratory pause," which is holding your breath at the end of exhalation. This will give you a few seconds to get off the shot.

A bipod stand creates a stable position to shoot from. A sandbag can also be used to create a stable firing position. Always rest the fore-end—not the barrel—on the sandbag.

4–7 SIGHTING IN A FIREARM

Due to minute variations in the manufacturing process, no two weapons of the same type and model will have the same point of impact. Because of this, sighting systems are adjustable.

Before sighting in a firearm, consider that you will use valuable ammunition and the noise might attract Zombies. Sighting in a weapon is the process in which the sighting system of a weapon is correlated with the trajectory of its ammunition. It is beyond the scope of this manual to include procedures for every sight you may encounter; however, because the underlying principles are the same, with some experimentation and common sense you should be able to figure out most types you are likely to encounter.

COMMON SIGHTING TYPES

Open sights or "iron" sights are by far the most common type of sighting system you will encounter. They utilize either a notch or aperture in the rear and a blade or post in the front. They are effective as well as rugged and simple. They are often a back-up sighting arrangement for weapons with other sighting systems. Focus on the front sight. This will result in the rear sight and the target becoming blurry, but this is okay.

Optical sights, such as scopes and "red dot" devices, have the advantage of the sight and target being on the same focal plane. This keeps both the sight and target in clear focus. Scopes and some red dots also have the have the advantage of magnification. This allows for the precise targeting of deep-brain structures. However, scopes with large magnification values can suffer from reduced fields of view.

SIMPLIFIED PROCEDURE

Make a four-inch circle on a large piece of paper or cardboard. Fill the circle in completely with a marker, crayon, or paint. This is what you will aim at. Place the target roughly one hundred yards away. Assume a stable, supported prone position and fire three shots. As you shoot, do not attempt to correct for misses. The goal is a tight group that you can use as reference to adjust your sights, aligning the center of your group with the center of your target. With open sights, move the rear sight in the direction you want the group to move. With optical and electronic sights, use the dials on the top and side to adjust your group.

4–8 MAINTENANCE

Firearms of all types benefit from regular maintenance and cleaning. It is beyond the scope of this manual to provide instruction for the maintenance of all types of firearms. Instead, general principles are offered.

- If you are unfamiliar with firearms, do not disassemble your weapon for cleaning lest you are unable to reassemble it. Use a toothbrush to remove dust and dirt from the parts you can access.
- Wherever possible, clean the bore of your weapon from the breech (rear) end.
- Specialized cleaning equipment exists; strive to acquire the correct tools to maintain your weapon.
- Extreme care must be exercised when using improvised equipment to clean the bore of your weapon. Do not use steel for an improvised cleaning rod; choose brass, aluminum, or wood instead.
- An excellent improvised cleaner known as "Ed's Red" can be made from equal parts automatic transmission fluid, mineral spirits, kerosene, and acetone.
- Use lubricants sparingly.

4–9 FEAR OF FIREARMS

If you are afraid of firearms and happen to find one, always carry it with the muzzle pointed in a safe direction (for example, straight up or down). Do not place the weapon in your waistband or pocket. When you are in a secure location, perform an examination of the weapon at a quiet time of the day when you can devote your full attention to the task. Children should be asleep or instructed to remain seated and out of the way. Only one person should handle the weapon at any time. Remember that firearms can shoot through walls. You must be aware of the location of other people in your group or other groups (for example, if you are in an apartment building) and always keep the weapon pointed in a safe direction. When examining a firearm, keep in mind that its controls were designed for right-handed operation and are located accordingly.

4–10 TRAINING METHODS

Air pistols and rifles (BB and pellet guns) make excellent training tools as they can be used indoors and are very quiet. They are not useful for Zombie eliminating, but they can be used for killing rats and other vermin.

Summary

Firearms are the best choice for eradicating the Zombie threat. They are simple to operate and easy to learn. Pistols and shotguns are best for close-quarter targets; rifles are best for medium to long-range targets.

Skill with firearms results in the ability to stay calm during stressful situations. These hunters were confident enough to gun down Zombies at close range because of their prior experience, knowledge, and familiarity with their weapons.

[Photo courtesy of Rob Sauerman.]

communicate with your neighbors

Weapons are the key to self defense in this new harsh environment. Weapons come in many shapes and sizes and are limited only by your imagination. In addition to firearms, there are three types of effective weapons: impact, blade, and stake. Impact weapons work by bludgeoning, blade by cutting, and stake by penetrating.

5–1 IMPACT WEAPONS

Every Zombie eliminator should be armed with an impact weapon suited to his or her size and strength. Impact weapons are key elements in your arsenal because they are easy to find or make, and they require no ammunition. They are silent, so they will not attract more Zombies. However, using an impact weapon requires significant strength and skill, and the user must be relatively close to the target. Other considerations include:

• **Impact weapons can fling Zombie fluids.** You must wear protective clothing, a face mask, and safety glasses when bludgeoning Zombies. Bystanders should also wear protective gear or stand far enough away so they do not get contaminated.

• **A weapon's weight can be detrimental.** A weapon that is too heavy will be unwieldy and slow you down—

OTHER WEAPONRY

IMPACT WEAPON **BAT**

Baseball bats can be effective in weakening or splitting the skull and eliminating a Zombie with direct strikes. Oblique strikes may not break the skull. Do not stop smashing the skull until the Zombie stops moving.

very undesirable traits when rapid, repeated strikes are required.

• **Impact weapons can be enhanced with small projections, such as bolts, nails, or screws.** These projections will help focus the impact and shatter and crack the skull. Once the skull is cracked, it will be much easier to destroy the brain. Zombie hunters should take care, however, when using long spikes on their impact weapons. Long projections may get "hung up," or stuck, in the skull. This can be especially dangerous if the weapon is attached to the Zombie hunter by a wrist strap.

• **A wrist strap is recommended if the weapon is in no danger of "hanging up."** If feasible, attach some kind of wrist strap to the end of the weapon to prevent you from dropping it during combat.

• **Baseball bats are ideal impact weapons.** Baseball

IMPACT WEAPON **CROWBAR**

Crowbars can be effective in splitting the skull and eliminating a Zombie with a direct strike. Do not stop smashing the skull until the Zombie stops moving. They can also be used to remove manhole covers to access subterranean routes.

bats are readily available and come in a broad range of sizes and weights to suit any Zombie hunter. A small aluminum bat can be wielded with one hand if necessary and can deliver a crushing blow. Other effective weapons include axe or pick handles, hammers of sufficient size, riot batons, crow bars, and plumbing pipes.

Replica swords are not built to be effective in actual use. Do NOT attempt to use them.

5–2 BLADE WEAPONS

Blade or edged weapons can be effective for eliminating Zombies, but they require skill to use and carry a risk of self injury. If you do not have confidence with a weapon of this nature, use an impact weapon instead. Bladed weapons come in two basic varieties: heavy bladed and light bladed.

HEAVY BLADED

A heavy-bladed weapon, such as an axe, has the capability to crack a skull due to its sheer mass. When using this type of weapon, aim to crack the skull using a downward stroke on the very top of the skull.

BLADE WEAPON AXE

Axes can be effective for splitting or smashing the skull with a direct strike or for severing the spinal column at the neck. Oblique strikes may not break the skull. Axes can "hang" if stuck in the bone of an attacking Zombie.

BLADE WEAPON **MACHETE**

Machetes can be very effective for severing a Zombie's spinal cord at the neck. Do not stop hacking at the neck until the Zombie collapses.

LIGHT BLADED

A common light-bladed weapon is a machete. Light-bladed weapons generally do not have the capability to crush the skull and destroy the proper amount of brain matter and, therefore, are not effective in direct assaults on the skull. They are better suited to severing the spine by attacking the area between the first and third cervical vertebrae (in the neck).

Consider the following:

• **Blade weapons should not be thonged or "dummy corded."** Edged weapons are prone to getting stuck, or hanging up, in your target. Ensure you can easily let go and free yourself from the offending Zombie.

• **If your weapon hangs up in the brain case of a Zombie, wrench down sharply.** This should free the weapon. Do NOT attempt to free it by pulling directly backward; doing so will draw the Zombie closer to you, increasing the risk of a bite. Do not hesitate to abandon a stuck weapon; you may be able to retrieve it later.

• **When sharpening your weapon, resist the temptation to create a "razor's edge."** It is possible to have a weapon that is too sharp, leaving the edge

BLADE WEAPON SAMURAI SWORD

Authentic Samurai swords are supreme Zombie-killing weapons. If properly sharpened, they can decapitate very effectively—and they are silent. Beware of fakes (which are fairly prevalent); they cannot be sharpened to the degree necessary for proper Zombie elimination.

vulnerable to rolling over or breaking. A bevel of roughly 10 degrees per side is ideal.

SIMPLE SHARPENING TECHNIQUE

Tool sharpening is a skill that is developed through practice. Heavy-bladed weapons, such as axes, hatchets, and machetes, can be sharpened with a long, smooth file. As previously mentioned, avoid the temptation to produce a razor's edge or an edge that is too thin. An overly sharp edge is prone to rolling over or breaking during heavy use.

Knives and lighter blades are sharpened on a whetstone. Imagine that you are trying to shave off a thin layer of the stone. Be sure to work both sides equally. Whetstones should be used with oil to prevent the stone from being clogged with metal particles.

5–3 STAKE WEAPONS

You can successfully eliminate a Zombie by "staking" its eye socket with a pointed weapon. Stake weapons should have at least five inches of penetration capability, and they must be robust. Common stake weapons include fire pokers, thin copper tubing, and ski poles (with baskets removed). Spears can fashioned out of broom, mop, or

STAKE WEAPON LONG SCREWDRIVER

Screwdrivers–or any type of stake weapon–can be used to penetrate the brain through the eye sockets, effectively re-killing a Zombie. Screwdrivers are portable and multifunctional and should be in every Zombie killer's arsenal.

rake handles by narrowing one end (at least five inches in length) and sharpening it to a point.

Piercing an eye socket requires close proximity to a Zombie and is considered an advanced tactic for Zombie elimination.

STAKING TECHNIQUE

When staking a Zombie, wear heavy-duty gloves, and make sure your wrist and arm are well protected. Once you have pierced the eye socket, drive the weapon as deep into the skull as you can. If possible, wrench up and down and sideways to expand the wound. Once enough brain matter is destroyed, the Zombie will go limp.

5–4 BOWS & CROSSBOWS

The foremost advantage bows and crossbows offer over impact and edged weapons is that you do not need to be close to the Zombie to eliminate it. They are silent, and the arrows can be re-used. However, a near-perfect shot is required to pierce the skull. Bows may be better used for creating distraction. Bows and crossbows can be used to create long-distance distractions (LDDs) when using ammunition-enhanced arrows. In either case, an archer should always have a back-up weapon.

OTHER WEAPONRY

RANGED WEAPON BOW

Bows or crossbows of sufficient strength can be effective in silently splitting the skull and eliminating a Zombie with a direct strike. Oblique strikes may not break the skull. Reloading takes time.

See **APPENDIX A: DISTRACTIONS** for more information on ammunition-enhanced arrows.

GENERAL CONSIDERATIONS

- Do not attempt to shoot a bow without either a glove or a release. Damage to your fingers will result. A release is a device that holds the string and provides a handle for drawing the bow. A lever or trigger is provided to release the shot. Never release a bow string without an arrow. It will damage the bow and might injure you.
- Always know what lays beyond your target. Arrows can ricochet off skulls.
- Arrows should impact the skull as perpendicular to the skull as possible. Shots should be directed to the sides of the skull, and shots to the forehead should be avoided. Shots to the rear, below the occipital bone, can be effective. Shots to the rear of the skull above the occipital bone should be avoided. The eye socket is a viable target.
- Bows of all types are not be fast enough to employ in horde situations.
- Most bows are not interchangeable between right- and left-handed users. If you are right-handed, you will hold the handle of the bow with your left hand and draw the string with your right hand. Left-handed users need a left-handed bow. (This does not apply to crossbows.)

- Archery can be practiced silently if you have the proper means for stopping the arrows safely. Several bales of hay are ideal. But you can improvise a backstop by stuffing cardboard boxes with packing material. Exercise care because modern bows are extremely powerful. Always be aware of what lays beyond your target.

TYPES OF BOWS

- Recurve bows and longbows are difficult to master. They are most effective when shot instinctively (without sights), can be reloaded quickly, are quieter than the quietest compound bow, and can be used with any type of arrow.
- Compound bows are easier to operate than recurve bows. They require less strength to achieve the same power, can be held at full draw for longer periods of time, and utilize precise aiming systems.
- Crossbows are very powerful and can be held at full draw indefinitely. While some crossbows utilize pin or iron sights, most are equipped with optics or electronic sights. They take longer to reload than either compound or traditional equipment and may require a special cocking device. Crossbow bolts are less common than other types of arrows.

ARROWS

- Aluminum and carbon-fiber arrows are the best choice, if available. Wooden arrows should never be shot from cross or compound bows as they are liable to explode upon release of the string. Aluminum arrows can be straightened if bent.
- Arrows can be retrieved. Rubber gloves should be

CHAPTER 5
OTHER WEAPONRY

used for protection when retrieving arrows that are contaminated with Zombie fluids and tissues.

- Retrieved arrows contaminated with Zombie fluids or tissues must be rinsed in hot, soapy water and disinfected in bleach for at least 10 minutes prior to reuse.
- The same points and broad heads suitable for conventional bows can be used with crossbows.

5–5 UNCONVENTIONAL WEAPONS

There are currently three unconventional techniques for Zombie elimination: incapacitating, crushing, and burning.

INCAPACITATING

The threat a Zombie represents can be reduced using methods that remove limbs or destroy significant amounts of body mass.

Incapacitated Zombies can still bite and spread VRV by the transfer of fluids.

If time permits, destroy the brains or sever the spines of Zombies with traditional methods once they are subdued.

CRUSHING

Crushing is a technique that can be simple and effective. Dropping a heavy item, such as a refrigerator, from a second story window can destroy or incapacitate a Zombie. Running over a Zombie with a heavy-duty vehicle or steam-rolling a Zombie with heavy construction equipment are also effective methods.

OTHER WEAPONRY

UNCONVENTIONAL WEAPON CHAIN SAW

Chain saws cut through flesh and bone with relative ease but must be used with protective headgear. Any blood that splatters into your mouth or eyes will result in infection. The noise will attract Zombies within earshot. Chain saws can be used to destroy frozen Zombies.

BURNING

Molotov cocktails can be used to set Zombies on fire. Typically, the brain will fry within an hour once the entire body is consumed by fire.

Setting Zombies on fire is generally NOT recommended as a method of elimination because the fire could spread to surrounding buildings or objects.

However, in certain circumstances, fire is acceptable. Consider these options:

• Molotov Cocktails

Molotov cocktails can be made by filling a glass bottle with gasoline or other highly flammable liquid such as turpentine or paint thinner. Stuff a rag into the mouth of the bottle. (Make sure the rag fits tightly in the neck of the bottle.) The rag acts a wick, much like the wick on a outdoor tiki torch. To put it into action, light the rag on fire and quickly throw the bottle onto pavement or any hard surface that will break it. This will cause the wick to ignite the fuel stored in the bottle and create an explosion. You can add thickening agents such as Styrofoam, rubber cement, or grated soap to increase the viscosity and adhesiveness of the flaming fluid.

• Zombie Corrals

There have been reports of Zombies being corralled into remote buildings or swimming pools and then torched. This technique was inspired by the eradication method of gypsy moths during the northeastern gypsy moth scourge of 1978, in which gypsy caterpillars were gathered on newspapers and set ablaze.

See **CHAPTER 20: ZOMBIE HUNTING** for more information on burning Zombies as a form of eradication.

5–6 CLEANING WEAPONS

After any contact with Zombies, remember to clean your weapons (and yourself) properly. Bleach is believed to be the best choice for cleaning weapons. Use a toothbrush to clean hard-to-reach areas. Bleach must dwell on surfaces for at least 10 minutes to ensure disinfection.

5–7 AUXILIARY TOOLS

SPRAY PAINT

Spray paint can be used to blind a Zombie at close range. Spray paint should be directed toward Zombies that are

UNCONVENTIONAL WEAPON EXPLOSIVES

Explosives, such as dynamite or pipe bombs, can be used to incapacitate Zombies and reduce Zombie hordes. Explosives can be thrown into areas that are inaccessible to gun fire. Discharges will attract Zombies within earshot.

OTHER WEAPONRY

stuck at fences or barricades or being controlled with a yoke—not used as a primary attack.

FORKS AND YOKES

In close-quarter combat, Zombies can be controlled with pitchforks, spading forks, or yokes. These devices are recommended for teams of two or more Zombie eradicators and are best suited for use with slower Zombies—but a fit, experienced team should be able to employ them against any type of Zombie. These devices are used to control the direction of Zombies or to pin them against walls or on the ground where so a second team member can employ a weapon against the skull.

• **Pitchforks** can be found in rural areas where animals are kept. Ensure the handle and shaft are free of cracks, splits, or other damage. With some creativity, new handles can be fashioned using the old handle as a pattern. Engage Zombies in the neck or abdominal area just below the rib cage.

• **Spading forks** may be more common than pitchforks because they are used in many home gardens. They are shorter but sturdier than pitchforks. Be aware that the shorter handle of a spading fork may allow Zombie contact if used incorrectly. Spading forks should be used

AUXILIARY TOOL SPRAY PAINT

Spray paint can be used to blind Zombies as well as to mark areas where Zombies are confined, such as locked rooms or houses. Spray paint can also be used to mark routes and make signs to communicate needs visually over long distances.

AUXILIARY TOOL **FORKS**

Pitchforks and spading forks can be used to control Zombies while other team members eliminate them. The longer the handle is, the safer the tool is, but the shorter spading fork can be more easily used in tight quarters.

only to engage the neck, Engaging the abdomen may allow the Zombie to double over and bite your hands or forearms. Longer handles can be fitted using the old handle as a pattern.

• **Yokes** are improvised devices that can be fashioned from nearly any type of material. Use a yoke to engage a Zombie at the torso, just under its armpits.

Keep the force of the Zombie in line with the fork or yoke and yourself. Adjust your stance as the Zombie changes direction. At this range, protection from blood and fluid spatter is essential; wear face protection such as a paintball mask or goggles and a bandana.

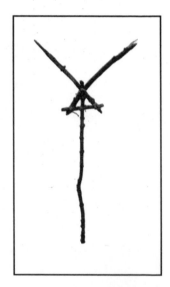

Use a yoke to control a Zombie while other members of your team re-kill it.

OTHER WEAPONRY

ROPE

Rope can be used to create tripwires or tie Zombies to an anchor, such as a telephone pole. Roping Zombies requires three people and at least 25 feet of strong rope.

Roping is not effective when there is more than one Zombie in the area.

Two people hold the rope on either end, and the third person attracts the Zombie's attention and leads it to the center of the rope. The rope handlers then pull the Zombie against the anchor (for example, a tree, street light, or telephone pole) and tie the Zombie to the anchor by circling it with the rope at least five times and then knotting the rope securely. Roping should be practiced only by well-protected, strong, and fit survivors.

See **APPENDIX B: TRIPWIRES**

5–8 HAND-TO-HAND COMBAT

Hand-to-hand combat is not recommended but may become unavoidable. When employing hand-to-hand combat, try to separate yourself from the Zombie by pushing or pinning it face down on the ground while remaining on top of it. If its mouth is facing the ground, it will have difficulty biting you. A Zombie wearing a tie may be easily pulled into this position. Once the Zombie is on the ground, release from it and attempt to escape to a safe location.

Do NOT punch a Zombie in the face. You should avoid its mouth at all cost.

Do not use religious icons in an attempt to turn the walking dead.

5–9 WEAPONRY THAT DOESN'T WORK

- Tasers
- Chains
- Torches
- Nunchaku
- Chemical weapons, mace, pepper spray
- Love
- Religious articles and icons

See **SEE CHAPTER 21: ETHICS & BARTER** for more information on Zombie Rights Organizations regarding the misuse of love as it is applied to Zombies.

Summary

Weapons capable of eliminating Zombies can be found in any home. Impact weapons are the bread and butter of close combat with Zombies. They knock them back, are easy to use, and can effectively crack the skull. A baseball bat is an ideal impact weapon. Bladed weapons should be used with caution, but can be highly effective if used with skill and confidence. Axes work as both a bladed weapon and an impact weapon and can be employed against the skull. Machetes and very large knives can be used to cut into the spine on the back of the neck. Stake weapons can be used to attack the eye sockets of a Zombie. Common stake weapons include broom handles and heavy duty screw drivers. Auxiliary tools such as forks, yokes, spray paint and rope can effectively aid in Zombie combat. Effective weaponry is only limited by your imagination.

Edged weapons can hang up. This Zombie survived when the axe got hung up in its clavicle and shoulder joint and could not be retrieved. The survivor who tried to eliminate this Zombie was most likely bitten and infected by the VRV.

[Photo found in camera]

Even chain saws can be ineffective for eliminating Zombies. This picture shows a fresh Zombie that was cut in half with a chain saw. Though the Zombie had no legs, it could still move and represented a threat.

[Photo courtesy "Saundra's Soldiers"]

Zombies can be tied to trees, telephone poles, or other anchors. This renders them ineffective without firing weapons. These Zombies were tied and even decorated by their captors before being photographed.

[Photo courtesy "86 Rangers"]

Religious symbols have no effect on Zombies. This priest attempted to turn back the walking dead with a crucifix. The video footage proves that his tactic did not work. Overconfidence blinds you to the realities on the ground.

[Footage found in video camera]

complacency kills

You can dramatically increase your chances for survival by simply not repeating the mistakes others have made. Below is a list of common mistakes people have made that led to their demise. Learn from them.

• Do NOT use love as a weapon to defeat Zombies.
Although they retain some of their basic memory, Zombies are no longer the people they were when alive. Any previous control you may have had over them is gone. You must learn to disassociate from the reanimated Zombie that is intent on killing you regardless of your previous relationship with the host.

• Do NOT try to blend in with Zombies to avoid attack.
This technique will work only if you cover yourself in rotting flesh and are a very convincing actor. It's not recommended. However, some gorilla costumes have been reported to work.

• Do NOT ingest alcohol or mind-altering drugs.
Any substance that impairs your ability to think clearly will only make you more vulnerable to attack. Substance abuse also proliferates depression and anxiety.

• Do NOT stand in front of windows.
Zombies are constantly looking for movement. They recognize human silhouettes. Light reflected from eyeglasses, jewelry, or a shiny button, for example, will draw their attention. Stay out of their view.

• Do NOT produce light at night.

Zombies tend to be more active at night. They are constantly seeking humans to bite and will seek out anything that produced light.

• Do NOT climb trees for safety.

Although climbing a tree during a Zombie attack might seem to be a good idea, it most assuredly will result in your death. The attacking Zombie(s) will gather at the base of the tree and, unless distracted by closer prey or eliminated by a fellow survivor, wait for you there indefinitely.

• Do NOT play music out loud.

It may be tempting to play music to relieve stress, especially for children or young adults, but any noise will attract Zombies. Listening to music with headphones should be done only if you are within sight of unimpaired survivors who can warn you in the event of an attack.

• Do NOT raise your voice in anger.

Being able to control your emotions is essential for survival. If you lose control and shout at someone for any reason whatsoever, you are not only endangering your own life by attracting Zombies that are within earshot but also the lives of everyone around you.

• Do NOT have unprotected sex.

Getting pregnant during the Zombie apocalypse is not a good idea. A pregnancy will dramatically decrease your chances of survival. Form relationships based on a potential Zombie-free future.

WHAT NOT TO DO

• Do NOT become overconfident.
Individuals who feel they are in control of their environment often become overconfident in their ability to predict outcomes, often with fatal results. Remind yourself that there are elements in every situation that you cannot control. Never assume that you are safe.

• Do NOT trust local authority.
Traditional authorities have been infected in droves.

Summary

It is an honor to those who went before you to learn from their misfortunes. Do not judge their decisions. Instead, take them as a sign of your own human ability for errors in judgement. Bear this in mind when planning missions. Use it to fuel your desire for redundancy and contingency planning.

Do NOT climb a tree. Although Zombies cannot climb trees, they will wait for you indefinitely. Zombies never sleep.

[Photo found in camera left at the scene]

Do NOT drink alcohol. These impaired students had no idea the Zombie, illuminated by the camera's flash, was approaching.

[Photo found in camera left at the scene]

WHAT NOT TO DO

Do NOT make moral distinctions with Zombies. Neighbors watched while this police officer was bitten because he could not shoot a "little girl."

[Photo courtesy of Chad Martinez]

WHAT NOT TO DO

Do NOT trust medics. Hospitals have become breeding grounds for VRV. If this nurse was allowed inside, the person who took the picture would not be alive.

[Photo courtesy Michael Williams]

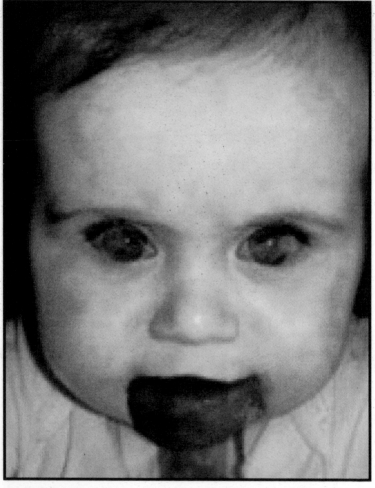

Do NOT breast feed your baby if you are a Carrier. You will transfer the disease through your milk. This child became extremely dangerous very quickly.

[Photo courtesy "D from Stroudsburg"]

how is your health?

What you wear during the Zombie apocalypse plays a critical role in your survival. There are many considerations, including temperature, relative safety, and weight. Overheating is a real concern and should be considered if you are expecting potential prolonged action.

If you reside in an area prone to mosquito activity, it is strongly advised that you use a bug spray containing DEET and sleep inside or under mosquito netting. There have been reports that the VRV has been transmitted by mosquitos. This is not something that can be reproduced in our labs, but researchers have hypothesized that if a mosquito bites a recently infected person while fresh blood is still present, the mosquito may be able to transmit the virus.

7–1 GENERAL CONSIDERATIONS

- Avoid light colors, or stain light colors with dirt or paint to darken them. Camouflage clothing is ideal.
- Cover as much skin as possible to help protect yourself against Zombie bites.
- Avoid overly tight and overly loose clothing that might hamper your mobility
- Break in new boots or shoes gradually.

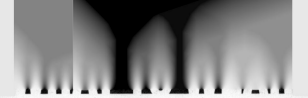

SURVIVAL ITEM **BANDANA**

Bandanas have many uses. They can provide mouth, neck, and ear protection. They can be used as a water filter or as a means to bandage a wound. Bandanas can also be used to keep sweat off your brow.

Bite Percentages:
Head & Neck — 43%
Arms & Hands — 37%
Legs & Feet — 15%
Torso — 5%

7-2 SAFE AREAS

A secure dwelling is a place where the possibility of a Zombie attack or a breach of the perimeter is extremely low. A blinded house is considered a secure dwelling. A barricaded house is ideal. In either case, you should never consider yourself 100 percent safe. You should always dress in a manner that allows for a quick and effective escape given an unforeseen Zombie attack or disastrous event, such as a fire.

• **Head & Neck**
GOOD: bandana, hair net, hat
BAD: not wearing anything

• **Hands & Feet**
GOOD: running shoes (best with ankle support), hiking boots
BAD: flip-flops, anything with high heels, sandals, bare feet

• Torso & Arms
GOOD: long-sleeved shirt
BAD: bare skin, short-sleeved shirt

• Legs
GOOD: jeans, comfortably snug long pants
BAD: shorts, exceptionally loose-fitting or tight pants

7–3 DANGEROUS AREAS

If there is risk of a Zombie attack, dress for it. Any time you venture outside your home base, assume that you are in a dangerous area. Always be prepared for the worst.

• Head & Neck
GOOD: paintball goggles or mask (eye and face protection), bandana or hat covering hair, bandana covering neck
BAD: jewelry

• Hands & Feet
GOOD: leather gloves with fingers, running shoes (with ankle support), hiking boots
BAD: bare hands, heels, flip-flops, bare feet, rings, jewelry, brightly painted nails

• Torso & Arms
GOOD: leather, rugged long-sleeved shirt, jacket
BAD: cotton shirt, short-sleeved or sleeveless shirt

• Legs
GOOD: knee pads, comfortably sturdy pants
BAD: restrictively tight pants, shorts, overly loose pants

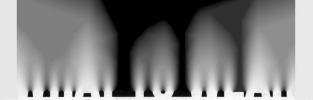

7–4 IMPROVISED ARMOR

Improvised armor will give you greater defense against bites. A canvas or leather neck protector can be fashioned out of a belt, tote bag, or piece of upholstery with a minimal amount of work. Layers of heavy cloth can be wrapped around the forearms to provide additional protection for more commonly exposed areas. If you feel encumbered or your mobility is reduced, use less material. Common sense should be your guide.

7–5 WEATHER CONSIDERATIONS

When planning to travel, carefully study the environment before venturing out, and consider the following:

MILD WEATHER

When on the move in mild weather, do your best to strike the proper balance between protection and ventilation.

COLD WEATHER

In cold weather, wear layers if possible. If it is cold and windy, wear an outer shell to protect against the wind.

RAINY WEATHER

If it is raining, take an extra set of clothing in a plastic bag.

HOT WEATHER

Avoid venturing outside on hot days. Overheating is a very real danger, and the nature of the required protection generally includes heavy clothing.

<u>Summary</u>

Dressing appropriately for your environment will increase your chances of survival. Protect your skin from possible Zombie bites at all times and in all environments. Wear bug spray if mosquitos are active. Always wear shoes that allow for easy escape. When going on a mission, consider the weather. Do not perform missions on hot days.

How to dress   vs   How NOT to dress

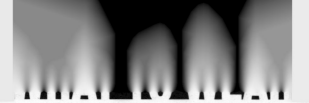

Fashion plays no role in your survival during the Zombie apocalypse. A woman paid with her life for wearing high heels when this Zombie attacked her and chewed her foot off.

[Photo courtesy Bam*Bam*Boys]

speak with clarity

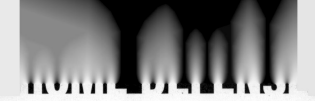

Making your home base safe—and creating your base of operations within it—will greatly increase your chances of surviving the Zombie apocalypse. There are three levels of home defense: locked, blinded, and barricaded. The model for this chapter is a two-story home with a basement.

8–1 FIRST LEVEL OF DEFENSE

The most important thing to consider when establishing a home base is not to attract (more) Zombies. Avoid attracting Zombies by keeping out of sight at all times. Crawling is the easiest way to prevent detection and should allow access to the entire house. Darkness affords even more freedom. Close and lock all doors and windows in your home, including doors inside the home.

Remove any visible pictures or posters that feature images of humans. Zombies are attracted to images of humans.

When your home is locked, do your best to defend it properly. Take your time and consider the best place in the building to use as a base of operations.

8–2 ESTABLISH BASE OF OPERATIONS (BOO)

Your BOO is the safest place in your home base. It should

be a room or area that can be isolated from Zombies if a breach occurs. Ideal qualities include:

• Two Exits

Both exits do not need to lead off the premises; for example, one could be a door that leads to the kitchen. One exit should, however, lead to the outside of the home.

• Obscured Windows

Windows located at ground level (basement windows) or well above eye level (second story) afford visual reconnaissance while maintaining anonymity. A second story BOO has reconnaissance advantages but requires a proper exit plan to make it safely to the ground outside.

• Insulation

Staying warm through the winter will be a test for many. A basement is often an ideal choice due to the natural insulation.

• Access to Tools and a Work Area

Garages can be ideal.

Once your base of operations is established, take a rest. In general, the longer you remain out of sight, the greater the chance that any Zombies outside will become distracted away from your home by other events.

While staying out of sight, stock your BOO with weapons and enough water and food to last two days. Once this is accomplished, consider additional weapon options. Take your time. When you are properly rested and have fully considered weaponry, begin the second level of defense. See **CHAPTER 16: EXIT STRATEGY** for more information on making elevated exits.

8–3 BLIND WINDOWS

Your first home improvement task is to blind every window in the building. Blinded windows greatly reduce your chances of being seen. Before blinding each window, cautiously look outside to determine if there are any Zombies lurking.

If you see a Zombie outside your window, do NOT attempt to blind the window. Abandon the plan temporarily; do your best to relax and calm yourself, and then try a different window.

Blind windows with existing curtains, mini blinds, or shutters first. If a window does not have an opaque covering, blind it with towels or blankets, quietly holding them in place with thumbtacks or by tying them to nearby fixtures. Avoid using a hammer and nails to blind the windows. Do your best to blind the entire house, covering each window and door only when you are certain you will not be detected by Zombies.

Be aware that blinds do not work at night if you happen to stand between a light source and the blinded window. You will create moving shadows, a primary draw for Zombies.

Once you successfully blinded all the windows without

SURVIVAL ITEM **HAMMER**

Hammers are necessary for quickly barricading a window. They can also be employed as a weapon and can effectively crack the skull and destroy the brain with repeated strikes.

Zombie detection, you have made your home "blinded clean," which is ideal. If your area is teeming with Zombie activity, you are finished with your home improvements until the Zombie density thins out. If your area has less than one or two Zombies in sight, consider construction of the third level of defense: barricades.

8–4 BARRICADES

Barricading your home base provides a defense that you can rely upon given unexpected circumstances and is recommended. Barricades are beneficial in many ways:

- Increase your peace of mind.
- Increase your ability to safely give refuge to other survivors in exchange for information or to barter goods.
- Provide more options for exit strategies when going on missions for supplies.

When considering a strategy for barricades, base your decisions on allowing for more avenues of exit and shutting down unnecessary rooms. Rooms that are not adjacent to an exit can be sealed off (or used as a quarantine room if you expect to receive refugees). Make sure to remove all valuable supplies from the rooms before sealing them off.

There are two types of barricades: doors and windows. Doors are much easier and safer to barricade than windows and can be performed by one person.

Barricading a window is an activity suited to two or three people. One person hammers while the others hold the pieces of wood or other materials in place.

Barricading can attract Zombies and should be considered a risky maneuver. Perform this task only when you are confident that it is safe and you can succeed. Always judge the situation by what you see on the ground.

BARRICADING DOORS
Doors can be easily barricaded by nailing them shut. Angle the nails so they substantially pierce both the door and the door frame. Make sure your nails penetrate through and into the frame at least half an inch. The longer the nail, the better. Doors that swing into the house can be barricaded with heavy furniture. Doors that swing out away from you can be tethered shut by tying a piece of rope to the door handle (using at least a double knot) and then securing the other end of the rope to an anchor, such as another door opposite the door you are securing.

BARRICADING WINDOWS
Procure enough wood to barricade the target window. Possible sources for wood include studs from interior walls, furniture, cabinet or closet doors, or other found sources. Interior doors, however, should not be used. If you cannot find enough wood, consider using steel bed

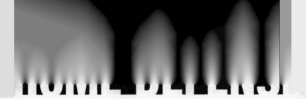

frames or shelving units. Use your imagination. Other preparations include:

• Gather a hammer or screwdriver. Both have been reported to work. Nails are loud and quick; screws are quieter but slower and may require a hand drill. Hammer and nails are recommended.

• Dress for a possible Zombie attack.

• Make sure all doors inside your home are closed and locked except doors leading from your barricading location to your BOO.

• Gather visual reconnaissance. Lift the blind and peer outside to make sure there are no Zombies close by. If it is clear, begin construction.

Construct your barricade by nailing boards horizontally across the area, leaving approximately six-inch gaps between boards to conserve supplies and allow for visual reconnaissance. Barricades need only reach a height of eight feet. Whoever is best with a hammer calmly and confidently hammers the nails while one or two people hold the board in place. When you are finished barricading one window, do a complete check on all rooms in the house.

See **CHAPTER 7: WHAT TO WEAR** for more information on dressing appropriately.

THREE CHOICES IF YOU ATTRACT ZOMBIES

• Finish Barricading

With two or more people, you may be able to hold the wood in place long enough to secure it.

• Fall Back

If the Zombie threat is stronger than your team, retreat to your BOO. Seal all doorways enroute. If the window you attempted to barricade leads to a sealed room, lock it down.

• Eliminate Zombies

If you believe you can effectively eliminate ALL offending Zombies, do so. Be sure to clean up and bleach any resultant Zombie fluids. Bleach must dwell for at least 10 minutes on surfaces to be disinfected. Wear gloves. Eliminated Zombies should be pushed or dragged outside the house, if possible. If this is not possible, they should be dragged into a room that can be safely locked or barricaded.

8–5 BLOCKADES

Hallways can be made impassable by piling heavy furniture into a stack large enough to block the passage. Stairways can be blockaded the same way, especially if Zombies are being prevented from going up the stairs.
If a Zombie is prevented from going down the stairs, it is much more difficult to effectively block them. As a general guide, use an entire living room set to block a single hallway or stairway.

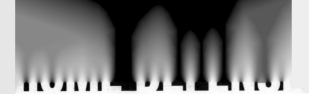

8–6 HOME VARIATIONS

APARTMENT BUILDING (NOT RECOMMENDED)

Benefits Include:

- Access to high points for long-range vision
- Possible access to large, flat roof for collecting rain water

Drawbacks Include:

- Few exits for the number of people
- Possibly many people in building to feed, manage, and trust
- If the building is breached, infection can spread extremely quickly

FARM HOUSE (IDEAL)

Benefits Include:

- High probability of wood-burning stove
- Old-world technology
- Access to many tools and weapons
- Stables can be used to contain Zombies
- Access to high points for long-range vision
- Isolation

Summary

Establishing a safe home will reduce stress and aid in your survival. Take your time and make home improvements as they become available to you. First lock all doors and windows. Then blind all doors and windows. Finally, lock unnecessary rooms and barricade doors and windows to rooms that lead outside or have a particular benefit.

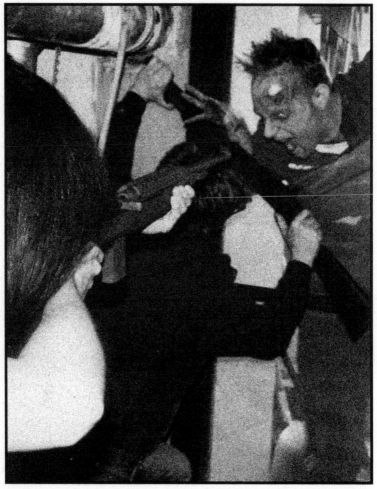

Screen doors are easily breached. Luckily these survivors had a backup plan when they attempted to barricade this door.

[Photo taken from surveillance camera footage.]

Photographs of humans will hold Zombies' interest. This Zombie stayed glued to this door for several days before the inhabitants realized it was trying to attack a poster of Keira Knightley. When the poster was removed, the Zombie disappeared overnight.

[Photo courtesy of Alley Getz.]

Most windows shatter easily. This Zombie banged its head repeatedly on this window until it broke. Blind your windows. Zombies will lose interest if they cannot see a human target.

[Photo courtesy Julie Luongo]

Mark areas where Zombies have been contained. Spray paint is a quick and effective marking tool.

[Photo courtesy James Scott]

talk about the Carrier nature

The purpose of a kit is to have the items that are essential to your survival in one bag that is light enough to carry without impairing your ability to run efficiently. You must fight the urge to carry unnecessary items. Your kit should be at your side at all times.

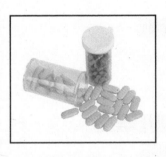

Vitamins and painkillers are useful, light and take very little space in your kit.

9–1 KIT CONTENTS:

FIRST AID

- Analgesic (pain reliever): Usually ibuprofen or codeine. Dosage varies.
- Intestinal sedative (pills, not liquids): For treating acute or chronic diarrhea. Imodium is a common brand. Dosage is two caplets, and a caplet after every passage of stool.
- Antibiotics: If antibiotics can be obtained, they are valuable for treating common infections. Antibiotics are NOT effective against the VRV.
- Antihistamine: For allergies and reactions to bites or stings. Brands include Benadryl, Claritin, and Sudafed.

Drowsiness is a side effect of some antihistamines.

- Antibacterial ointment: A generic bacitracin ointment can prevent infection and speed the healing of wounds.

- Butterfly sutures: For holding the edges of a wound together.
- Bandages: For controlling bleeding. Obtain a wide variety of sizes.
- Bleach: A staple of any survivalist's kit, bleach can be used to purify water and sterilize areas that are potentially contaminated with VRV.
- Medical tape
- Water purification tablets
- Any required medicines

9–2 KIT CONTENTS: HYGIENE
- Toothbrush/toothpaste
- Bar soap
- Nail clippers

A lighter is handy for starting fires, lighting cigarettes, and use as a signaling device.

9–3 KIT CONTENTS: SUSTENANCE
- Can opener
- 1/2 gallon water
- Energy or candy bars
- Jerky
- Tea bags, flavored drink powders
- Multivitamins
- Salt

9–4 KIT CONTENTS: TACTICAL
- Heavy duty screwdriver: To pry open doors and stake Zombies.
- Knife: An all-purpose item.

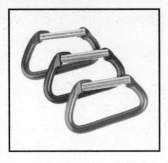

Carabiners are handy to use for trip wires, harnesses, or zip lines.

- Length of cord or rope: For setting up trip wires or traps, corraling Zombies, or escaping from buildings.
- Whistle: To intentionally draw Zombies toward you.
- Matches or lighter: To create fire or light cigarettes.
- Permanent marker: To create signs for communication.
- Laser pointer: To distract Zombies.
- Flashlight: To illuminate, communicate, or distract Zombies.
- Spray paint: To mark Zombie locations or blind Zombies.
- Journal: For noting Zombie behavior, self reflection, and planning.
- Small mirror: To look around corners safely or use as a signaling device.

Summary

Your kit allows you to quickly escape any situation with all the necessary equipment to survive. Strive to make it light, keep it in good order, and always have it close at hand.

there is tragedy in everyone's life, not just yours

Communicating with friends, family, and fellow survivors without drawing the attention of Zombies has many benefits. Connecting with fellow human beings expands your world, creates the possibility for the exchange of goods, and provides a greater sense of purpose. All forms of communication require a sender, a message, and an intended recipient. Various effective techniques exist.

10–1 GENERAL CONSIDERATIONS

AT HOME

If you are in a safe area—meaning one in which you are not at immediate risk of being attacked—verbal communication is appropriate. Speak only as loud as needed to communicate effectively. Be careful not to "talk above" other survivors by raising your voice. If you believe that people are speaking too loudly, gently remind them that they are putting themselves and you at risk. When communicating, do not mumble. Speak clearly.

FROM HOME

The easiest and safest way to communicate with your neighbors or nearby survivors from your home base is to create written signs and display them from an elevated position, such as a second-story window. At night, light signals are best but only if both the sender and the recipient know Morse Code. (A Morse Code chart is located at the end of this chapter.)

IN FIELD
When outside, in field, verbal communication could endanger your life; use extreme caution. Whispering or using hand signals can be safe and effective methods of communication between teammates. Common hand signals that everybody knows are the "OK" symbol and the thumbs-up or thumbs-down. To communicate with strangers, use a portable sign kit.

10–2 WRITTEN MESSAGES
Written messages are rarely misunderstood and completely silent. They are ideal for communicating with your neighbors. Print your messages using large block letters so they are easy to read. Send messages from an elevated position, if possible. When sending a message, hold the sign up long enough for the recipient to read it. When receiving a message, let the sender know it was received by giving them a "thumbs-up."

Consider the following:

SURVIVAL ITEM BINOCULARS
Binoculars are most effective at higher elevations. They can be used to study Zombies and the surrounding the area. Binoculars allow you to read messages from a distance and can be used to assist marksmen.

COMMUNICATION

• Use easily understood shorthand to save space without confusing your recipient. Below is some common shorthand that is easily understood within a message, even to someone who is unfamiliar with it.

2 = too, to
2MORO = tomorrow
2NITE = tonight
4 = for
B = be
B/C = because
WILCO = will comply
W/O = without

C = see
PLS/PLZ = please
RU = are you
B4 = before
U = you
UR = you are
W/ = with
R = are

• When your message is completely transmitted, hold up a sign that says "end of message."

• If you have trouble reading a message, hold up your own sign explaining the problem; e.g., "Handwriting 2 small."

SIGN KIT

You may want to create a portable kit of words or phrases that you can put together to form the most common types of messages you want to send. This is especially helpful when going on a mission. A typical sign kit might include the following words and phrases. (Areas that can be covered to change the meaning are shown in parentheses.)

Hello, my name is...	How the hell are you?
Seeking trade(?)	Yes, No(t), OK
Arrow signs ← →	Thanks
Have, Need	Medic(?), Food(?), Help(?)
Want to talk?	Entry, Exit
Can we visit?	Good(bye)

There should always be blanks and a marker in a sign kit.

SEMI-PERMANANT SIGNS

Constructing a semi-permanent message out of opaque tape or paint can be effective for broadcasting an ongoing alert or request. It has been reported that survivors who painted "need insulin" on the side of their second-story home were helped by another survivor who delivered it to them. Once your problem is solved, or if you vacate the location, be sure to take the sign down or paint over it.

10–3 SIGN LANGUAGE

American sign language is a highly effective method of non-verbal communication. It can be used to fill in the blanks left by traditional hand signals and allows complex messages to be delivered silently and effectively. This can be especially effective when combined with the use of binoculars. (A chart of the sign language alphabet is located at the end of this chapter.)

10–4 LIGHT SIGNALS

Flashlights have been reported to work effectively for

COMMUNICATION

SURVIVAL ITEM FLASHLIGHT

Flashlights are effective for illumination and communication as well as for creating a distraction. Light attracts Zombies, so when carrying a flashlight in field, turn one battery backward to prevent yourself from accidentally turning it on at an inopportune time.

communicating with Morse code. (A chart on Morse code is located at the end of this chapter.)

FLASHLIGHT MODIFICATIONS

Reducing the side emissions of your flashlight will allow you to focus the light beam to your recipient more precisely. Construct a cone around the lens out of paper or cardboard and tape to limit the direction of the light. If you are venturing outside, wrap opaque cellophane or construction paper in front of the lens to dim it.

Artificial light draws the attention of Zombies. Do not use light to communicate outside at night except in emergencies. When in field, whispering is the preferred method of communication.

If you are too far apart to whisper and conditions permit, consider using a flashlight. Use quick flashes and a simplified code to reduce the amount of light you produce. Transmit short messages using only one, two, or three short flashes. (Establish what these signals mean in advance.) Wait at least 10 seconds between messages.

ELEVATED CHANNELS

When communicating with light from safe areas, signal

from high elevations to avoid attracting Zombies. (Zombies generally do not look up.) Stand approximately four feet away from the window when flashing the light. This will help create a tunnel effect directly to your recipient, concealing the light from those whom should not see it (i.e., Zombies). In general, whatever you can see from the point of view of your flashlight is what can see the light you are flashing. Blind all windows in the room except the one you are using. Redundancy is a key to your survival.

MIRRORS IN THE LIGHT OF DAY

Using a mirror to transmit messages is a proven yet simple technology. A mirror can be used with Morse code for complex messages. (Any shiny object can be used, but for best results use a mirror or a bicycle reflector. CDs or DVDs are only about 25 percent as effective as a mirror.) Mirror signals can be transmitted up to 10 miles away on a sunny day. They can also be transmitted at shorter distances on overcast days and even at night when there's a full moon. A mirror is used by holding it toward the sun and reflecting the light toward the recipient.

10–5 RADIOS

CITIZENS' BAND (CB) RADIOS

CB radios salvaged from commercial vehicles are an excellent means of long-range communication. A CB radio has multiple channels, so the sending and receiving radios must be set to the same channel. There may be multiple parties using the same channel, so use call signs to identify yourself. Keep radio traffic to a minimum; short, concise messages are best. If you wish to transmit private information, use pre-determined code words or phrases.

COMMUNICATION

HAM RADIO

Ham radio (also known as amateur radio) operators are of vital importance to long-range communication. The ham radio community has long been active in disaster relief and therefore is likely to be prepared for emergency situations. The ham radio network circles the globe and is currently the best method of monitoring the worldwide Zombie situation. If you are a ham operator, please consider helping your community. Community members are urged to support ham operators with their missions.

10–6 MOBILE PHONES

At the time of this writing, no cell phone towers are in working condition. As conditions stabilize, the cell towers should begin working again. If you have a cell phone that still has battery life, conserve the battery by keeping it turned off except to check the signal once a week.

If you discover cell service, consider the following:

• Keep the ringer off and vibrate on to avoid attracting Zombies.
• When making a call, remember that the person may not have turned off the ringer, which could be dangerous.

10–7 GOVERNMENT BROADCAST

The government is currently developing a broadcast message program. The broadcast will cover all major spectrums and will transmit updates on the Zombie situation as new information becomes available.

10–8 MAIL

Mail is still a relatively reliable mode of communication due to the efforts of the "Order of the Appointed Round" (O.A.R.), a militant organization of fanatical letter carriers from the U.S. Postal Service. The O.A.R. is dedicated to providing uninterrupted mail service at any cost. Their range is unknown at this point, but consider checking with your local post office. Stamps are still being honored, but in lieu of postage a small donation of fuel, food, or ammunition will ensure that your mail is delivered.

The O.A.R. asks that dogs be kept under control and that the areas around mailboxes be kept free of booby traps, obstacles, and debris.

Summary

Communication is a key to your survival. Different circumstances require different methods. Study all available methods and use them when appropriate. Written signs and sign kits are convenient and effective. Light signals can travel long distances. Elevated positions are preferred. Radios will help us rebuild our communities. Science will prevail.

CHAPTER 10

COMMUNICATION

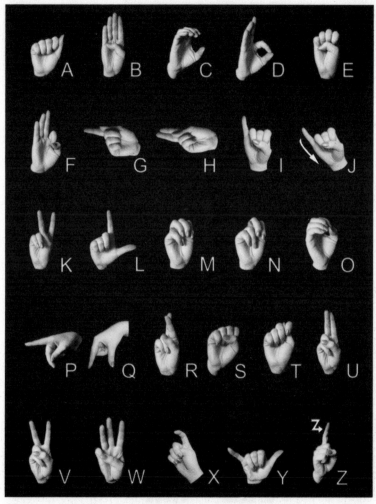

The American sign language alphabet is a highly effective and silent form of communication. Over time, efficiency quickens interactions. Increase your range with binoculars or scopes.

MORSE CODE

	American	International
A	• —	• —
Ä		• — • —
Á		• — — • —
Å		• — — • —
B	— • • •	— • • •
C	• • •	— • — •
CH		— — — —
D	— • •	— • •
E	•	•
É		• • — • •
F	• — •	• • — •
G	— — •	— — •
H	• • • •	• • • •
I	• •	• •
J	— • — •	• — — —
K	— • —	— • —
L	——	• — • •
M	— —	— —
N	— •	— •
Ñ		— — • — —
O	• •	— — —
Ö		— — — •
P	• • • • •	• — — •
Q	• • — •	— — • —
R	• • •	• — •
S	• • •	• • •
T	—	—
U	• • —	• • —
Ü		• • — —
V	• • • —	• • • —
W	• — —	• — —
X	• — • •	— • • —
Y	• • • •	— • — —
Z	• • • •	— — • •
1	• — — •	• — — — —
2	• • — • •	• • — — —
3	• • • — •	• • • — —
4	• • • • —	• • • • —
5	— — —	• • • • •
6	• • • • • •	— • • • •
7	— — • •	— — • • •
8	— • • • •	— — — • •
9	— • • —	— — — — •
0	——————	— — — — —
@		• — — • — •

how is your kit?

Infants, children, the elderly, the sick, and domestic pets present a variety of unique concerns during the Zombie apocalypse. Each dependent has unique needs, liabilities, and assets. Study this information whether you are currently in a situation of this type or not. You will likely encounter one in the future. Plan for contingencies.

11–1 INFANTS

Infants require feeding and constant care, but they are the future of humankind, so they should be a priority. An infant is best kept at a single location. If supplies are needed for an infant's survival, it is best to keep the infant at your secure location with an adult while other adults go on a mission to retrieve the appropriate supplies.

If you must move an infant, carry it in a backpack or hand-held tote or in your arms. Armored child carriers that are bite- and gnaw-proof can be fabricated from pet carriers. A bicycle with a basket can be modified to carry a baby at high speeds but should be used with caution. A vehicle is ideal for transporting an infant. Be sure to secure the baby in the vehicle—there is a high probability that you will have to make quick decisions while driving.

Do not use a baby carriage or stroller to transport a baby because they are cumbersome and loud.

11-2 EMERGENCY CHILDBIRTH

There are very few doctors available, and most hospitals have been overwhelmed by Zombies. If a woman gets pregnant, she will most likely have to give birth with the help of other survivors and whatever materials are available. Fortunately, delivering a baby is a relatively simple procedure that people have been performing since the beginning of humankind.

The model in this book is for two people—the expectant mother and one person who will deliver the baby (you).

WHAT YOU'LL NEED
• Scissors or a knife
• Boiling water to sterilize a knife or scissors
• Multiple blankets or towels
• Sheet, tarp, plastic garbage bags, or newspaper
• Comfortable pillows
• Thread, twine, or thin rope
• Sealable container or large bowl

CHOOSING AND PREPARING THE AREA

Choose a birthing room based on safety. The mother will most likely moan, scream, or cry out loudly, and the baby may cry when it arrives. A room without windows in the center of the building or a basement are ideal. Prepare the area by placing sheets on the floor and gathering the necessary supplies. Sterilize a knife or scissors in boiling water for at least 10 minutes. Use blankets and pillows to make the mother as comfortable as possible during labor. To be safe, have an extra pillow nearby that the mother can use to muffle her screams.

WHEN YOU KNOW IT'S TIME

Hard labor signifies imminent birth. Time the contractions from the beginning of one to the beginning of the next. Once they are about five minutes apart, move the mother to the birthing room and prepare to deliver the baby. When the contractions are less than two minutes apart, birth is imminent. It is normal for the mother to feel anxious or panicked during this stage of labor. Do your best to calm her down by showing confidence in your desire to safely deliver the child and letting her know that her emotions are perfectly normal.

STEP-BY-STEP GUIDE TO DELIVERING A BABY

Step 1: Have the mother lie down on the floor. The baby will be slippery, so you want it to be as close to the ground as possible. The mother can lie on her side during labor, but when the birth is imminent, have her lie on her back, spread her legs, and partially sit up in a squatting position assisted by pillows.

Step 2: Wash your hands for several minutes with soap and water and/or an antibacterial hand sanitizer.

Step 3: Support the mother during the contractions. Prop her up and have her take slow, deep breaths. The mother should push between contractions to slow the process, but it is okay if she also pushes during contractions. Do not be concerned if she screams or groans loudly; give her a pillow to muffle her cries. Encourage her to blow through her mouth at the peak of each contraction.

Step 4: Look for the emergence of the baby's head (this

is called "crowning"). If a membrane (the amniotic sac) is stretched across the head, pinch it and twist to break it. (The membrane usually breaks on its own but sometimes requires assistance.)

Do NOT pull on the baby's head, the umbilical cord, or any part of the baby.

Step 5: Guide the baby. As the head comes into view, gently support it with your hand to prevent it from popping out too quickly. The baby will come out in waves with the contractions. Support the baby throughout the process. As it emerges, the newborn will most likely turn to the side naturally. Apply some gentle pressure on the base of the vagina near the perineum to help baby's head pass.

Step 6: When the head fully emerges, gently remove excess mucus and amniotic fluid from the baby's nose and mouth. The mother should stop pushing at this point to give you the time to clean the infant. If the umbilical cord is wrapped around the baby's neck, try to gently loosen it and slide it over the baby's head. If you cannot move the cord, simply continue delivering the baby.

Do NOT cut the umbilical cord yet.

Step 7: Catch the baby. Once the baby's shoulders emerge, the rest of the body will come out quickly and be quite slippery. Hold the baby securely with the feet higher than the head. (Do not hold the baby by its feet.) Allow the fluids to drain from the baby's nose and mouth.

Step 8: Place the baby face down on the mother's stomach or chest with full skin contact. The baby's head should be slightly lower than its body to help drain the mucus. Cover them with clean blankets or towels. If the baby is blue, do not panic. Remove excess fluids from its nose and mouth and make sure it is breathing. If it doesn't breathe immediately, gently slap the soles of its feet. If that doesn't work, gently administer CPR.

Step 9: After the baby is delivered, the placenta will be expelled on its own. This may take from a few minutes to a half hour. Before the placenta is fully delivered, blood will flow from the vagina. Gently rub the mother's stomach below her belly button to slow the bleeding. If the mother is willing and able, have her nurse the baby immediately. This helps to expel the placenta and reduces the bleeding, but it is not essential. Once the placenta is fully delivered, place it in a container.

Do NOT try to assist the delivery of the placenta.

Step 10: Now it is time to remove the umbilical cord. First feel the umbilical cord for a pulse.

Do NOT cut the umbilical cord if it has a pulse.

After about 10 minutes, the pulse will stop. Only then should you cut the cord. Use clean thread and a double knot to tightly tie it off approximately four inches away from the baby. (The mother and infant will not feel any pain from this procedure because there are no nerve endings in the umbilical cord.) Tie it off a second time about four inches away from the first knot. Then cut the cord between the two knots using the sterilized scissors or knife. (Do not be surprised if it is difficult to cut.)

Step 12: Reduce the mother's pain and clean up. Administer pain relievers to the mother, if available. Encourage the mother to urinate. Use a pan or allow her to urinate on the ground cloth. When she is ready, move her and the newborn to a bed. Feed and clean the mother as needed. Place all resulting fluids into a sealed container.

Step 13: Dispose of the placenta. Zombies are attracted to the smell of blood and human fluids; the placenta is no exception. If your home is not barricaded, strongly consider going on a mission to dispose of the placenta in an area far from human habitation. If your home is secure, consider storing the placenta for use at a later date; it would make a good distraction for Zombies.

BREECH BIRTH
If the baby comes out feet first, gently move the mother to an elevated position, such as a bed. Have her sit on the edge, and place pillows and blankets on the ground below in case the baby falls during the delivery. Push the mother's knees toward her chest.

Do NOT touch the baby until the head comes out. Your touch may stimulate the baby to breathe, resulting in suffocation.

Be ready to gently catch the baby once its head comes out. Then follow steps 7 through 13 above.

11–3 CHILDREN

Children are assets in this trying time; they should be taught the skills they need to survive at every given opportunity.

Give them responsibilities that match their capabilities, and be patient: All skills are mastered through practice.

Familiarize children with the tasks and missions you undertake to sustain your group. You can make a game out of many lessons.

Starting and maintaining a fire is an excellent task for children to undertake. Skills such as using and caring for edged tools, load management, and planning are ancillary to starting and caring for a fire.

If you have a BB gun or air rifle, take the time to teach them marksmanship.

Children's toys must be silent. Make sure that any sounds are muffled. Noises such as bells, squeakers, and buzzers must be disabled.

Do not use the threat of Zombies to get children to finish their vegetables.

11–4 THE ELDERLY

The needs of elderly people can vary widely, from checking in on them occasionally to hand-feeding and constant care, but they are far from useless in most situations. The elderly can excel at providing comfort, planning a mission, or even sniping. Respect the wisdom they've gained from hardships they have endured.

In this difficult time, the elderly are best kept to a single location. If supplies are needed for an elderly person's survival, it is best to go on a mission to retrieve those supplies.

The limited agility and movement of an elderly person can slow down the entire group.

If you must bring an elderly person on a mission, understand that if you are attacked by Zombies, you may have to leave the person behind during your escape. Unfortunately, it does not make sense to sacrifice the lives of younger people to save an elderly person in this new harsh environment.

11–5 THE SICK

The needs of the ill vary widely depending on the illness, but some general rules apply to most situations:

• Confine sick people to an isolated room, if possible. If one is not available, confine them to one side of a room.
• Give them something to do that will benefit the group. Having a purpose reduces suffering and aids in recovery.
• Have them cover their mouths with masks or bandannas.
• If you do not have the appropriate medication, consider communicating with your neighbors and informing them of your situation. They may be able to help.

- If a person's condition becomes life threatening, consider going on a mission to obtain the medication or services needed. Be sure to take your highest trade-value items to exchange for the medicines or services you seek.

Avoid hospitals because they have become breeding grounds for the VRV.

11–6 PETS

All pets are useful in keeping up morale and relieving stress, and they are a possible food source in emergencies.
Pets, like all animals, are not recognized by Zombies.

Cats kill rodents, help to conceal scent, and fend for themselves.

CATS

Cats can hunt for themselves and kill rodents. Male cats can spray areas with human-concealing scent. Moving them from one location to another, however, is not practical if you are on foot. Transport cats with a vehicle.

DOGS

Dogs require feeding, which is a disadvantage when supplies are scarce. Most breeds need daily exercise, which requires a safe fenced yard.

A barking dog will attract Zombies.

Some dogs can be trained as watch dogs or guard dogs and add a good nose to your arsenal. Watch dogs are those that are trained to bark if a breach is made into your safe zone. Nearly any breed of dog can be trained to do this. Guard dogs are those that are trained to attack on command. The best guard dogs are large dogs that are easily trained and have a natural inclination to protect their owners.

If your dog is not well trained and barks incessantly, it may be best to kill and eat the dog.

HORSES

A horse can be an asset if it is well trained and its rider is skilled. (The rider must be capable of keeping the horse under control during a Zombie attack.) Zombies will recognize a human being astride a horse and are not intimidated by the horse. Therefore, it is important that the horse be calm. (Thoroughbreds and Arabians, for example, are generally too high strung; quarter horses and draft horses are known to be more docile and are generally preferred.)

Owning a well-trained horse has several advantages:

- A horse elevates the rider, making it much more difficult for Zombies to effectively bite the rider.
- Horses can navigate most obstacles far better than most vehicles.
- Horses disguise human scents and can "cover your tracks" with manure.
- Horses are able to transport additional supplies.

• Horses do not require fossil fuels, such as gasoline.

If you are a capable rider with a reliable horse and you decide to travel by horse in field, be sure to wear boots and protective clothing. Consider improvising armor for your ankles and legs.

Horses should NOT be ridden by amateurs in this chaotic landscape except in emergencies.

<u>Summary</u>

Every person has a role to play in continuing the survival of the human race. The elderly bring wisdom. Children are eager to learn. The sick want to contribute. The infants of today will lead us to the dawn of a new era for humankind. Even pets can be an asset in this hostile environment.

emotions are contagious

Maintaining healthy habits is a key to your survival. Do your best to develop these habits over time. Make your goals for adopting habits manageable. It takes time and persistence to successfully change bad habits and develop good ones.

12–1 PERSONAL HYGIENE

Good personal hygiene is the most important thing you can do to prevent illness and avoid Zombies. (Strong body odor will betray your presence to Zombies.) But in this challenging environment, water is at a premium and must be conserved. Always take care to use as little water as possible when maintaining your hygiene. Do not take showers or baths. The following regimen should be maintained to both stay clean and conserve water.

ON A DAILY BASIS
• Wash your hands
• Brush your teeth

ON A WEEKLY BASIS
• Clean your entire body with soap and a wet cloth
• Clip your fingernails and toenails

HUMAN WASTE
A toilet can be improvised with a five-gallon pail lined with a plastic bag. Keep the pail covered when not in use.

CHAPTER 12

SURVIVAL HABITS

Odor can be controlled with cat litter, sawdust, or baking soda. Toilet paper can be substituted with newspaper, pages from a book or telephone directory, or even paper currency. Dispose of the bags away from your location.

12–2 STRETCHING

Stretching relieves stress and makes you less prone to injury. It can help improve your running ability, which can save your life. As a general rule, do not stretch cold muscles. If you are cold, warm up first by doing some jumping jacks, running in place, or skipping rope. Stretch before and after working out. Stretch before going on missions. Do not overstretch. A simple rule is to stretch to the point where you feel uncomfortable but not to the point where you feel pain. In general, hold stretches for approximately 15 seconds. Do not bounce. Stretch both sides of your body.

Do not stretch injuries that have not fully healed.

• **Quadricep Stretch**
While standing, bend your left leg and use your right hand to grasp your foot or ankle behind you. (Hold onto a stationary object with your left hand if necessary.) Hold your heel toward your buttocks, keeping your back straight and left knee down. (Do not let your left knee extend forward.) Repeat with the other leg.

• **Hamstring Stretch**
Sit on the floor with your legs extended and feet together. Raise your arms above your head and slowly reach for your toes.

• Hip Stretch

Lie on your back, knees bent with feet flat on the floor. Lift your left leg and place your left ankle on your right thigh, just below the knee. Grasp the back of your right thigh with both hands, and pull your right knee toward your chest until you feel a stretch in your buttocks and hips.

• Calf Stretch

Place both palms against a wall at shoulder height, about shoulder-width apart. Step back with your left leg. While keeping your left heel on the ground, push your pelvis toward the wall until you feel the stretch in your left calf. Keep your back straight and your shoulders back. Repeat with the other leg.

Hand strength helps
with scaling walls and
overcoming obstacles.

12–3 EXERCISE

Developing strength and endurance is key to your survival. Never push your workout too far; you need to avoid injury and stay fresh in case of emergency. The following exercises are recommended to develop and maintain your core strength and improve your running ability. Do three sets of repetitions of each exercise three or four times a week for maximum benefit. Keep track of your progress in your journal.

• Push-Ups

Push-ups are the single most effective exercise in this book. If you do nothing but push-ups you will still be accomplishing a great deal. Push-ups increase the strength of your arms, back, and abdominals, and they provide cardiovascular benefits. Try to keep your body straight. If you cannot do push-ups, just hold the form for an extended amount of time without moving up and down.

• Crunches

Crunches strengthen your abdominal muscles. Crunches are similar to sit-ups but involve bending your knees toward your chest while lifting your chest toward your knees. If you have weak abdominal muscles, try resting your feet on a chair or keeping them on the floor while bending your knees. Focus on using your abdominal muscles rather than your back, leg, or neck muscles. Exhale as you sit up; inhale as you lie back down.

• Lunges

Lunges strengthen your quadriceps, buttocks, and hamstrings. Keep one foot in place and take a big step forward with the other while keeping your back straight. (Try not to lean forward.) Then bend your knees to lower your body straight down. Push off with your forward foot to return to a standing position. Repeat with other leg.

• Squats

Squats strengthen your thighs, hips, and buttocks. Stand with your feet about shoulder-width apart. Put your hands on your hips or hold your arms out in front of you. Slowly bend your knees, keeping your heels on the floor, your back straight, and your buttocks pushed back. Hold the position for a few seconds, and then stand back up. (You can also hold a weight in each hand during this exercise.)

• Heel Raises

Heel raises increase the strength in your ankles and calf muscles. Hang your heels over the edge of a step, holding a railing or using a wall for support. Raise your heels up and stand on your toes. Hold that position for a few seconds; then slowly lower your heels past the edge of the step until you feel a stretch in your Achilles tendons.

12–4 KEEPING A JOURNAL

Keep a journal to record your experiences, ideas, goals, and thoughts. Writing your own story will help you organize your thoughts and gain perspective on your situation. (Read your journal about once a month to monitor changes and gain insights.) Other benefits of journaling include the following:

• Reduced Stress

The act of writing down your experiences allows you to get past bad or stressful ones more easily.

• Increased Hindsight

It is easier to recognize patterns and changes in your attitude and behavior over a period of time.

• Improved Clarity

As insights are gained, goals come into focus.

• Increased Focus

When you understand yourself and determine your goals, you can focus better on attaining your objectives.

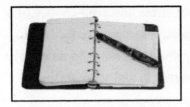

Notebooks can be used to plan missions, keep a journal, and record Zombie behavior.

12–5 ZOMBIE LOG

Start keeping a Zombie log to write down your observations on Zombies. Studying Zombies and recording their behaviors will help you predict future behaviors. Watch Zombies from a vantage point that prevents them from seeing you. Since Zombies generally do not look up, elevated positions are ideal.

Record the number of Zombies you see in your area twice daily: morning and evening. This is the Daily Zombie Count (DZC) of your location. Name and describe each Zombie spotted, rate its level of freshness, indicate its general location, and chronicle any specific behaviors that seem noteworthy. Feel free to draw a hypothesis or make predictions, but do not rely on your own guesswork. Confer with others before coming to conclusions on the nature of the Zombie universe.

See **APPENDIX D: SAMPLE ZOMBIE LOG** for a sample.

Summary

Good habits are the cornerstone to a successful lifestyle during these trying times; they will increase your effectiveness over time and ingrain themselves into your life. Proper hygiene reduces both stress and your chance of succumbing to or spreading illness. Stretching reduces the chance of injury, improves your ability to run, and reduces stress. Exercise increases your strength and your ability to run. Keeping a journal increases your focus, gives you proper perspective, and reduces stress. Keeping a Zombie log increases your understanding of Zombie behavior, thereby increasing your ability to predict future behavior.

strength of purpose reduces suffering

Time is on your side. Zombies are decomposing with each passing day. Gathering and conserving resources will extend safe time at home. Surviving the winter without power is an obstacle that must be overcome. Welcoming your neighbors or refugees into your home during this troublesome time can broaden your knowledge and foster goodwill.

13–1 WATER

Water is your single most valuable resource. Humans have been known to survive without food for as long as four to six weeks, but they cannot survive more than a few days without water. Dehydration causes your blood to thicken, which in turn causes your heart to work harder and results in a loss of circulation. Lack of water causes your physical and mental abilities to decrease substantially and rapidly.

If water is scarce, conserve the water in your body by remaining silent, resting often, staying cool, and avoiding eating or smoking.

POTENTIAL WATER SOURCES
• Outdoor streams, lakes, or puddles. When looking for natural water sources, remember that moving water is better than still water, and clear water is better than cloudy water.

- Canned food items often contain significant amounts of water. Do not drain this valuable resource. Drink it or use it as a base for soups or stews.
- Swimming pools are a potential source of water; however, disinfect pool water by boiling it for at least one minute; boiling may also help reduce chlorine taste.
- Toilet tanks can be a source of clean water.
- Garden hoses can be uncoiled and drained of water.
- Home water heaters can be drained and used, but water used for hydraulic heating systems might contain chemicals and should not be used.
- Beer and wine may used in moderation to extend water supplies; care must be taken to avoid intoxication.
- Caffeinated beverages, despite their reputation as diuretics, can be consumed as a water source.
- In an emergency, you can drink the blood of game animals or use their blood to dilute soups and stews.
- Do NOT drink antifreeze, salt water, or water that contains chemical contaminants.

Avoid water tainted with Zombie tissues or fluids. Zombie blood has been found to transmit the VRV even when diluted with water.

HARVESTING RAINWATER

Collecting rainwater is the best and easiest way to renew this most valuable resource. Rainwater is naturally occurring, free of contaminants, and if collected and stored properly can keep you hydrated year-round. The practice of collecting rainwater has been used since ancient times and the technology is proven. Commonly used systems are constructed of three principal components: the catchment area, the collection device, and the storage system.

• Rooftop Catchments

Rain gutters are ideal catchments for rainwater, but they must be kept as clean as possible. The first time you clean them, use disinfectant and scrub them as thoroughly as possible. Maintain them at least once a week. Cut back any overhanging trees, and look for areas with potential for frequent blockages. Direct the gutters to collection containers; then sift out any particulates before transferring the water to a long-term storage container.

Flat rooftops are generally safe from Zombie attacks, accessible, and ideal for collecting rainwater. Place clean containers of all sizes on the roof to catch rainwater.

• Ground Catchments

Any safe area that is exposed to the elements can be used to catch rainwater. Fenced yards are ideal. Place buckets, jars, or other containers in the area to collect rainwater. Use or create funnels to increase the collection area of the container. Devise drainage systems and dams to guide the flow of rainwater into buried containers. Use tarps to prevent water from soaking into the ground.

• Street Catchments

Streets usually have catchment systems (drains or gutters) already in place, but they are generally unsafe.

Street catchments could be contaminated with VRV and are not recommended.

An umbrella can be used to increase the catchment area of a container during a rainstorm. Cut a small hole in the canopy, around the center pole. Then add a counter-weight to the umbrella by filling a small plastic bag with something clean and heavy, such as small stones. Tie the bag to the center of the umbrella, and place it over the container, as shown below.

HARVESTING SNOW

Snow can be melted for water. However, a considerable amount of energy is required to melt snow and should only be considered if you are in desperate need of water.

WATER STORAGE

Water storage tanks should be able to be sealed to prevent contamination from animals and to preclude algae growth and the breeding of mosquitoes. Food-grade plastic or glass containers with reusable caps or lids are suitable.

For long-term storage, buckets and jars should be emptied into larger vessels that can be sealed. Stainless steel containers can be used to store water that has not been or will not be treated with chlorine (chlorine is corrosive to most metals). A clean, 55-gallon drum or trash can lined with a plastic bag is ideal.

SANITIZING CONTAINERS

First soap and rinse the containers. Then create a solution of one tablespoon of chlorine bleach per gallon of water. Soak the containers in the solution for two minutes; then rinse again with water. It may be difficult to remove every bit of residue from some containers; pay special attention to hard-to-reach areas, such as the handles of milk jugs. To sanitize a stainless steel container, place the container in boiling water for 10 minutes. Never reuse containers that previously held chemicals, poisons, or other hazardous substances.

FILTERING WATER

Water should be filtered whenever possible. With the possible exception of commercial water filters that are designed to remove microbial contamination, filtration will not remove all pathogens. It simply makes cloudy water more palatable. Water can be filtered by pouring it through paper towels, coffee filters, thin fabrics, or even clean sand.

DISINFECTING WATER

Disinfection kills harmful organisms in drinking water, making it safe to drink. Disinfection can be accomplished several ways:

• **Commercial water-disinfection tablets:** Follow directions on the package. The most common ratio is one tablet for one quart of water. Use two tablets if the water is cloudy or contains visible organic solids. After adding the tablet(s) to the container, wait three minutes and then shake the container vigorously. Wait at least 10 minutes before using the water. (At colder temperatures, wait at least 20 minutes.)

• **Boiling:** Heat the water to a rolling boil for at least five minutes.

• **Bleach:** Use 10 drops of bleach per gallon of water. Shake or stir the mixture vigorously and let stand for 30 minutes. If your container has a screw-top, loosen the top to disinfect the threads. You should be able to smell the chlorine in the water; if you don't, treat the water again and let it stand for 15 minutes. In moderation, the odor and taste of chlorine indicate safety. There is no appreciable harm from drinking mildly chlorinated water, but as a general rule do not drinks large amounts of chlorinated water in one sitting.

Swallowing or breathing the fumes of undiluted bleach can lead to poisoning. Use caution and keep bleach out of the reach of children.

• **Iodine tincture:** Use 20 drops of iodine per gallon of clear water and 40 drops in cloudy water. Mix or shake vigorously and let stand for 30 minutes before use.

• **Solar:** Ultraviolet light from the sun will kill harmful organisms. Pre-filtration is required when using this method as suspended particulate will inhibit the action of UV rays. Use only clear plastic water bottles with labels removed. (Glass and opaque or scratched plastic bottles may inhibit action.) Fill the containers with water and expose them to strong sunlight for a minimum of six hours; two to three full days might be required on cloudy or overcast days.

TASTE

Water that tastes stale may be improved through aeration. Shaking vigorously in a partially empty container should improve the taste. Plain black charcoal from wood fires will also absorb tastes and odors. Strain the water through the charcoal; then filter out any sediments and disinfect, if desired. Instant coffee, tea, bouillon cubes, or flavored drink powders can help make unpalatable disinfected water taste more agreeable.

Fresh fruits and vegetables have high trade value, provide valuable nutrients, and boost morale.

13–2 FOOD

Anything that walks, crawls, flies, or swims can be eaten, with one notable exception: Zombies. Insects and other related invertebrates have served as a food source from ancient to modern times in a variety of cultures throughout the world. Insects can be eaten as larvae, pupae, or mature adults.

EXTENDING RESOURCES

The amount of food a person needs per day to stay relatively healthy varies, depending on his or her age, weight, activity level, and gender. As a general rule, try to extend your food supply by never eating to complete satiation. While this may be difficult at first, your body will eventually adapt to this new regiment.

PLANTING A GARDEN

Planting a garden is a forward-thinking, excellent idea. Fresh vegetables will provide valuable nutrients, increase morale, and hydrate the body. They are also highly valuable in trade.

TRAPPING AND SNARING SMALL GAME

Small animals, such as feral dogs or cats, rabbits, squirrels, pigeons, ducks, and geese, can be caught with traps or snares, which are relatively easy to construct. Although you may be reluctant to eat some of these animals, you do not have the luxury of exercising your cultural food preferences. You should try to add fresh meat and protein to your diet, regardless of type.

• Snare

In its simplest form, a snare is a noose made of cord or wire that kills by strangulation. Place snares on game runways, through undergrowth. Check them once or twice daily. Arrange each snare so the animal is caught as it passes through. Bludgeon any snared animals that you find alive.

• Box Trap

Squirrels and certain birds can be caught with a box trap. A sturdy cardboard box can be propped up with a stick and baited with corn, acorns, or bread. When the animal is completely under the box, a string tied to the bait is pulled, collapsing the box and trapping the animal. Consider weighting the box with bricks or a flat rock to help contain the animal.

• Water Trap

Water fowl, such as ducks and geese, can be caught with a length of cord tied to a submerged rock or cinder block. The free end of the cord is outfitted with a fishhook or barb covered with floating bait such as a bread ball or a bit of flesh wrapped around a fragment of cork. The rock or cinder block is placed in the water, and the bait on the cord floats above, one to two feet underwater. When the bird swallows the bait, the bird will be tethered to the rock underwater and drown.

FIELD DRESSING GAME

Once you have killed an animal, it must be prepared for cooking and eating. Bacteria grow and spread quickly, so you must dress (gut, skin, and butcher) the game as soon as possible, generally in the field. Quickly gutting the animal is especially important because the internal organs keep the carcass warm, which fosters bacteria growth.

It is beyond the scope of this manual to provide instruction on dressing and butchering all types of game. Do not be concerned if you have never butchered an animal; there is no wrong way to do it, only neater and more efficient ways. If there are hunters in your group, have them teach what they know. If you are a hunter, share your knowledge.

Despite the common notion of a large "hunting knife," a small, sharp blade no longer than five inches is ideal. This is also true for butchering, although a saw or hatchet might be required to cut through bones.

Before you begin, ensure that the area is clear of Zombies. It has not been determined whether Zombies are attracted to the scent of animal blood. Do not allow yourself to become so engrossed in the task that you are unaware of your surroundings. If possible, a second person should stand watch.

• Removing Internal Organs

After you have killed an animal, the first job is to "gut" it (remove the internal organs) and begin cooling the carcass. The following instructions are for large animals.

Step 1: Using a small, sharp knife, cut around the entire perimeter of the anus until you can pull it free a few inches. Tie a cord securely around the rectum to prevent the feces from escaping.

Step 2: Make a cut from just below the anus, along the underside of the animal, to the throat. With male animals, cut around both sides of the penis and testicles. Take care not to nick the bladder and spill urine. (But if you do, simply wipe and rinse the body cavity well.)

Step 3: Remove the sternum by cutting or sawing at the junctures between the ribs and the sternum. Try to make as large of an opening as possible. Cut the esophagus and arteries of the neck.

Step 4: Find the diaphragm—a thin muscle attached to the circumference of the chest cavity behind the lungs— and cut it free.

Step 5: Grasp the lower intestine and pull the anus back through and out of the body cavity. (If feces are released, simply wipe and rinse well after you are done.)

Step 6: With the animal on its side, cut the remaining attachment points of the organs. Once free, they will come out in a mass.

Step 7: Wipe the cavity free of blood. Spread the cavity open with a stick to aid cooling.

Small animals can be cleaned with a cut from anus to throat. Grasp the organs firmly and pull free. Cut any stubborn attachments.

• Skinning

Skinning is the next step in processing animals for consumption. Once again, there is no "wrong" way, only easy and difficult ones. You can do this!

Step 1: With large animals, it is beneficial to hang them by their rear legs. Spread the legs with a stick

Step 2: To skin the legs, make a circumferential cut through the skin around the legs near the knees. Peel the skin away as you cut down the inside of the leg toward the body cavity.

Step 3: Remove the skin by peeling it away from the carcass.

Step 4: Coax stubborn points free with your knife.

For small animals, cut off the feet and make a cut near the neck so you can work your fingers between the skin and muscle. Grasp the skin firmly and pull the skin free.

Birds need to be plucked of all feathers, but do not skin them because the skin is rich in calories.

• Butchering and Preserving

The butchering of game is easier than you might think. The larger muscle groups are bundled with connective tissue and are easily freed with a few cuts. With everything else, the goal is to remove muscle from bone.

No butchering is needed for small animals. Roast or stew them whole or in quarters. Baste with oil.

Preserve what meat you can with kosher (non-iodized) salt or sea salt. Rub the salt into thin slices of meat and allow to dry in the sun and wind. If you don't have sufficient salt, meat can be sliced thinly and allowed to dry in the sun and wind. If the outside temperature is below freezing, the meat can be frozen.

Reserve the brain, heart, lungs, kidneys, and liver for stew meat. If any of these organs are spotted or look "off," do not eat them. These organ meats may be more palatable if minced fine and added to stews.

If you have killed a large game animal, consider inviting nearby, friendly survival groups for a meal rather than let the meat go to waste.

13-3 STAYING WARM

Human beings can survive in cold weather indefinitely if they make smart decisions and properly insulate themselves.

SELECTING A SLEEPING AREA

- Sleeping areas should be small to retain heat.
- Select a space away from prevailing winds.
- Avoid rooms with large windows or walls that are not insulated.
- Interior spaces without windows, such as bathrooms and closets, have low heat loss.
- Basements are naturally insulated by the earth.

INSULATION METHODS

- Insulate cracks in doors and windows with heavy drapes, plastic sheeting, blankets, towels, or anything else you can find.
- Beds are ideal for conserving body heat.
- Wear a hat at all times.
- Cover your mouth with a scarf or cloth to conserve the heat from your breath.

HEATING METHODS

• Fireplaces / Wood-Burning Stoves

Wood-burning stoves are ideal but require a chimney. If you do not have a wood-burning stove but have a chimney flue, you may be able to fabricate your own stove and attach it to the existing flue. If you do not have a flue, it may be possible to make a stove pipe that can be extended through a window to provide proper ventilation.

LONG-TERM SURVIVAL

SURVIVAL ITEM **PORTABLE STOVE**

Portable stoves provide heat to cook with wherever you go. They can also be used as a heat source but only as a last resort and with plenty of ventilation. Fuel is a premium resource and should be conserved.

Many older homes have capped stovepipe thimbles in rooms that were once heated by stoves. You may be able to remove the non-functioning furnace pipe from its flue vent and hook up a portable or improvised stove or heater in its place.

Use your imagination when constructing stoves and fireplaces. A thick layer of brick or stone should sufficiently protect a wood floor from the fire. Large metal containers serve well as improvised stoves. Punch or cut holes in the bottom to improve air flow. Cinder blocks and bricks can be stacked near a window to make an excellent fireplace. Make it wide rather than deep to maximize radiant heat.

A "hobo stove" can be constructed from a large metal can and used as an excellent cook stove.

• Kerosene Heaters
Kerosene heaters are very effective but must have adequate ventilation. Diesel fuel can be substituted for kerosene in most kerosene devices, such as lanterns, stoves, and heaters.

• Generators
Generators consume a lot of fuel. They cannot be

operated indoors and must be kept outside during operation. Generators are also quite loud; their sustained noise can attract Zombies. However, if you are isolated and have plenty of fuel, a generator can be extremely useful. Stale or old gas that is not suited for motor vehicle use may be suitable for the simple motors found in generators.

• Gas or Charcoal Grills

The least desirable solutions are makeshift heaters, such as charcoal burning or gas grills. If you must use them, do so with plenty of ventilation.

Unless you are able to properly vent them, do not use heaters or light fires indoors.

• Solar Heat

A significant amount of heat can be gained through large windows on the southern side of the dwelling. If your area is devoid of Zombies or has very few, remove some blinds to allow sunlight in. Consider moving to various locations in the building throughout the day. You may heat water in the sun for a warm shower or soup.

• Heated Bricks

Bricks and cinder blocks retain heat well and make excellent bed and feet warmers. Place bricks in or near the fire or stove. Once the bricks are very warm (but not hot), use tongs, protective gloves, hot pads, or towels to carefully remove them. Wrap the bricks in towels and place them near your feet or under the covers of your bed.

• Safety Considerations

Keep fire-fighting tools near your heating device. Fire extinguishers, sand, salt, baking soda, or water can be used on non oil-burning fires. A heavy blanket can be used to smother flames. Do not store fuels in heated areas.

All heaters and fires must be properly ventilated to prevent harm or death from smoke inhalation or carbon monoxide poisoning.

Drowsiness, dizziness, shortness of breath, mild nausea, and mild headaches are some of the early symptoms of carbon monoxide poisoning. Introducing fresh air into the room could be life-saving.

13–4 GATHERINGS & GIVING REFUGE

Inviting friends and neighbors into your home can be beneficial in the following ways:

- Stress reduction through stories and humor.
- Exchange of goods to round out supplies.
- Strengthening your purpose and capabilities if a bond is made.

If you plan to have a gathering, offer to meet your guests at their home base and guide them to yours as a polite gesture. Have a plan for safe passage. Consider serving them dinner. If you visit other survivors, take gifts.

GIVING REFUGE

Giving refuge is the act of welcoming unknown survivors

or groups that are on the move into your home base. Use caution when providing others with refuge.

Only welcome strangers into your home if you are sure you have the ability to kick them out.

Do NOT allow potentially infected survivors into your home. Check for bite marks.

Be wary of refugees who try to obscure a member of their own party, attempt to hide their arms or neck, or are excessively frantic.

If you decide to turn away an individual or group, let them know in no uncertain terms.

CREATING A QUARANTINE ROOM

If you decide to welcome strangers into your home, create a quarantine area to protect yourself. A quarantine area is place that can hold a small group of people securely. This can be a room or a fenced area. Whenever possible, the enclosure should provide the occupants with protection against Zombies. Quarantine the refugees for at least five minutes to fully allow for the potential manifestation of the VRV. (Death and reanimation from the VRV generally occurs within minutes after a bite.)

If an infection occurs during the quarantine procedure, do NOT allow the victim(s) to escape. Keep the refugees locked in the quarantine area and mark the door as having Zombies inside.

Darts is an excellent, silent game to pass the time while maintaining concentration.

POST QUARANTINE

Post quarantine is a chance for bonding and barter. Once the refugees have made it past quarantine and into your safe zone, introductions are in order. Discuss your experiences in recent weeks. Share local knowledge and any helpful information, especially regarding Zombie hordes and Zombie behavior. Afterward, discuss group intentions, needs, and barter. Consider eating and playing a game together.

Summary

There is a multitude of solutions to the problems of water, food, and warmth. Solving these should keep you busy and content. As the days pass, plan for a mission to retrieve supplies or, if you have the time and resources, consider hosting a gathering of friends. Consider giving survivors refuge if they seek it.

END PART ONE

PART 2
IN FIELD
ON A MISSION

CHAPTER 14
TEAMWORK

When going on a mission, it is best to go with at least one other person. Group members share responsibility and can carry out tactics not possible by only one person. The team members must work together effectively and cohesively to ensure not only their survival but also the survival of the entire group. A leader helps make a group more effective. Men and women are equally capable of fulfilling leadership roles.

14–1 CHOOSING A LEADER

For a group to be effective, it needs a leader. Sometimes choosing a leader is easy; other times it may be more difficult. Successful leaders share certain traits that make them effective. Everyone in the group should be aware of these desirable traits before electing the leader:

- Ability to control emotions
- Ability to communicate effectively
- Adaptability
- Extraversion
- Impartiality
- Intelligence
- Self-confidence

After everyone is aware of these traits, a vote should be

taken to elect a leader (if one is not evident). A tie can be decided by a coin toss. Everyone in the group must accept the leader, even if they did not vote for him or her. If someone is unwilling to accept the leader who has been chosen by the majority, that person must not be allowed to go on missions with the team.

If your mission group has more than four people, a secondary leader should be chosen by the group. This should be done by a vote in the same way the leader was selected.

14–2 LEADER RESPONSIBILITIES

The lives of group members depend on the leader's abilities. Leaders have the following additional responsibilities:

• Maintaining the morale of the group
• Keeping focused on the big picture
• Defining proper goals for the group
• Assigning proper tasks for group members
• Looking for ideas that move the group toward its goals
• Making quick decisions and communicating them clearly in stressful situations

CONTROLLING EMOTIONS

A survival group's emotions will generally follow the mood of their leader. Recognizing and controlling emotions is essential for leaders; it is a skill that can be developed. Recognize your emotions and accept them for what they are. Emotional intelligence—the ability to recognize and manage moods and emotions in one's self as well as other people—is an exemplary survival trait. The more members of the group who have this capability, the better the group will be able to function.

14–3 INDIVIDUAL RESPONSIBILITIES

Each member of a team is personally responsible for:

- **Purpose:** Knowing the goals of the team.
- **Priorities:** Knowing the importance of each goal as it relates to other goals.
- **Roles:** Knowing what his/her role is within the group.
- **Communication:** Exchanging information to keep the group informed.
- **Consideration:** Respectfully considering ideas from other members.
- **Resolving conflict:** Dealing with conflict openly and honestly.
- **Understanding the balance of contributions:** Accepting that not everyone will put forth the same effort at all times.
- **Success:** Recognizing when the team has achieved success.
- **Fitness:** Staying fit.

See **CHAPTER 12: SURVIVAL HABITS** for more information on fitness.

14–4 TEAM ROLES

Specific roles give members of the team a sense of purpose and something to focus on. Each role is assigned by the leader based on the particular member's skill set. Some common roles include:

TEAMWORK

- **Medic:** A person involved in the medical field—especially with emergency or first-response experience, such as an emergency medical technician, a paramedic, or a military member trained in battlefield first-aid.
- **Mechanic:** A craftsman who has the ability to diagnose and repair machinery.
- **Cook:** One who's skilled in making appetizing food out of sparse or unpredictable ingredients.
- **Fitness trainer:** One who is knowledgeable about physical fitness and has the skills motivate others.
- **Caretaker:** A compassionate person who's skilled in general care and comfort (for children, the sick, and the elderly).
- **Fabricator:** A craftsman with a creative mind and the ability to fabricate devices and solutions using the materials at hand.
- **Survivalist/Hunter:** A person trained in wilderness survival who can navigate, construct shelters, hunt, gather water, and prepare food in a wilderness setting.
- **Sniper:** A trained marksman who shoots targets from concealed positions or distances exceeding the capabilities of ordinary personnel.
- **Gunner/Shooter:** A person who's proficient with firearms.
- **Communicator:** One who's responsible for creating a sign kit for the mission. Knowledge of sign language or Morse code is ideal.
- **Archer:** Someone expert in the use of a bow and arrow.
- **Brawler:** A person of strength, capable of destroying or separating a skull with a blade or impact weapon.
- **Runner:** One who is naturally athletic and can run fast.
- **Carrier:** A carrier of the VRV.

CHAPTER 14
TEAMWORK

- **Spiritual leader:** Someone who is naturally positive and forward thinking.

See **CHAPTER 2: CARRIER NATURE** for more information regarding Carrier advantages and liabilities.

Summary

Teamwork is a cornerstone to your survival. For a team to work properly, it must have a leader. The leader helps maintain the group's morale and understands the goals of the team. The leader creates plans, assigns tasks, and makes decisions in field for the entire group. Everyone on the team supports the leader by being personally responsible for themselves. Team roles give members a clear purpose.

what is your responsibility?

CHAPTER 15
PLANNING A MISSION

Missions are planned around the goals of the entire survival group. Common goals include retrieving supplies, making a safe passage to a friend's or relative's home, or eradicating Zombies. The Zombie-infested landscape is fluid and ever-changing. Establishing a plan before going on a mission is essential for success.

15–1 MISSION TYPES

RECONNAISSANCE MISSION

This is an information-gathering mission, which could be as simple as taking a look down a street to determine how many Zombies are in the area. Reconnaissance missions are generally short and are often nested within other missions.

SUPPLY OR LOCAL RESOURCE MISSION (LRM)

If you have a properly barricaded or isolated home, it is most likely in your best interest to stay there. In this case, additional supplies must be retrieved from potential sources, such as abandoned homes and hot spots. Hot spots are areas of mutually shared interest with other survivors.

Assume there will be Zombies inside all abandoned homes and hot spots.

CHAPTER 15
PLANNING A MISSION

Indicators of an abandoned home include (listed in order of strength):

- Open windows or doors
- Not barricaded
- Not blinded

See **CHAPTER 16: EXIT STRATEGY** for more information on entering buildings.

See **CHAPTER 19: HOT SPOTS** for a list of hot spots and tactics for liberating them of their contents.

NEW HOME BASE MISSION

It may be in your best interest to move in with friends or relatives or to establish a new home base. (But consider that every member of your survival group will have to travel.) Some locations are better than others. Isolation from Zombies, natural defenses, resources, and proximity to resources all play a role in determining the value of a home base in this difficult time. In addition, a house with solar power would be ideal. There are two types of new home base missions:

• Abandoned Takeover

Take over and move into an abandoned home. An abandoned house could be an upgrade, which would improve your lifestyle.

• Merge

The best new home base can be one that is already occupied by friends or relatives. If you know them well

SURVIVAL ITEM PORTABLE GAS

Siphoning gas will be inevitable if you plan on using a
vehicle to travel. A hose, a funnel, and a storage container
are invaluable tools in your arsenal.

and can expect a hospitable welcome, the move may be
worthwhile. But consider that they may be running out of
supplies too. Also consider communication techniques
for when you arrive. Some successful merges between
strangers have been reported.

See **CHAPTER 11: DEPENDENTS & PETS** for more information
regarding concerns and tactics for moving infants and the
elderly.

LONG-RANGE MISSION

Although they are not recommended, missions of great
distance may be necessary. There have been reports of
successful journeys in excess of 100 miles. Long journeys
require a vehicle. Be prepared for breakdowns.

See **CHAPTER 17: VEHICLES** for more information on using
vehicles.

BASE CAMP MISSION

It may be advantageous to establish a secondary base
camp to extend your range and provide a place from
which you can launch other missions. A base camp is an
annex to your home base, and there should be a relatively
safe and familiar route between the two.

PLANNING A MISSION

See **CHAPTER 20: ZOMBIE HUNTING** for more information on missions that can be launched from a base camp.

15–2 WHEN TO TRAVEL
PREDICTING WEATHER
The weather can often be accurately predicted on the day of travel by using common sense. If it looks like it's going to rain, it probably will. Beware of dark, low, and dramatic cloud formations which often have an "anvil top." These signal heavy or extreme precipitation. If you notice a halo around the sun that's created by clouds, study it. Generally, if the halo gets bigger, fair weather is ahead; if the halo gets smaller, precipitation is on the way.

• Cool to Warm, Sunny Days
It is recommended that you travel by daylight in cool to warm, clear weather. It is not recommended to travel on hot days due to the propensity to overheat. Only travel in extreme cold weather if you are properly dressed for it.

• Rainy Days
Rain dampens noise and decreases visibility for both Zombies and survivors. If it is raining, or if rain is expected, stow everything in plastic bags. Garbage bags and freezer bags are ideal. Consider packing an extra set of dry clothing to avoid hypothermia.

NIGHT TRAVEL
Be aware of what phase the moon is in. Spend about 20 minutes in an unlit, safe area just outside your home base or base camp to allow your eyes to adjust. Try to relax. If

you are traveling by vehicle, drive with the lights off.

Night travel is best limited to one or two competent survivors.

Consider the following:

• Carry two flashlights. Reverse one battery in the spare flashlight to prevent turning it on accidentally.
• If a vehicle with its headlights on approaches you, cover or close one eye to protect your night vision.
• If traveling by vehicle, consider flashing your high beams at Zombies in your path as a blinding technique.
• Your eyes have greater clarity in the periphery at night. To see something better, look askance at it or sweep your eyes around.
• If you wear glasses, strap or dummy-cord them to you to prevent losing them. Carry a spare pair if you have them.
• If traveling at night with children, have the children hold on to a piece of rope or cord (e.g., a jump rope or extension cord) that is attached to an adult.

See **CHAPTER 10: COMMUNICATION** for information on communicating at night.

15–3 ROUTE SELECTION

Every mission has a route. The route you select is the single most important decision you make when preparing a mission. Look for ways to use natural features. Consider the following relatively safe routes:

WOODLAND

Wooded land does not attract Zombies. Additionally, it is generally difficult for Zombies to maneuver in the woods, especially if they are post mortis (PMZ). Consider woodland routes as mostly Zombie-free travel opportunities.

RIVER TRAVEL

Rivers and large streams provide a measure of safety from Zombie attacks. Zombies can walk underwater and do not breathe, but their movement is severely limited by water. Rivers with strong currents or depth will carry them away. Use caution if you are a novice to the skills involved in successful navigation of your vessel.

Use chalk to mark underground routes while on the move.

SUBTERRANEAN ROUTES

Underground passages, storm drains, and utility tunnels are an easily overlooked means of travel.

Beware of possible toxic gases and/or oxygen deficient atmospheres in any underground space.

Subways are likely to house multitudes of Zombies.

See **CHAPTER 18: ON FOOT** for tactics regarding subterranean routes.

PLANNING A MISSION

15-4 MISSION PLANNING, LEADER LEVEL

When planning a mission, begin with the end in mind. Consider what obstacles need to be overcome to attain your goal, and choose members that will be an asset to the mission. Do NOT travel with a woman who is menstruating. Zombies can smell blood. Determine the most logical and safest route to accomplish the mission, and allow plenty of time to achieve it. Consider disposing of trash and human waste generated from your home base during missions.

Leaders should always consider how other members may contribute to the planning process and ask for their input when appropriate.

GENERAL CONSIDERATIONS
- What is the objective of the trip?
- Will you travel by vehicle or on foot?
- What special tasks need to be performed?
- Which members of the group will go, and what role will each person play?
- What supplies and equipment are needed?
- Are there friends or relatives along the way that may be able to help?
- How much time is available?

USE OR CREATE A MAP
Maps are ideal for studying the terrain and features of the area in which the team will be operating.

A compass can help you orient yourself if you have a map to work with.

They make it easier to determine shortest paths. Maps can be found at gas stations, libraries, and bookstores. If you are already familiar with the area, you can make a map from memory. Whenever possible, collaborate with others to ensure accuracy. Evaluate your map or sketch for:

- Safe passages (woodlands or tunnels)
- Hot spots
- Areas of concealment
- Estimation of Zombie densities (areas around tall apartment buildings, colleges, hospitals, and discount retailers tend to yield high Zombie populations)

FINE-TUNE THE PLAN
- Prepare a sign kit for your mission
- Consider using distractions as a means to gain entry or assist in your goal.
- Study the route using binoculars from an elevated position.

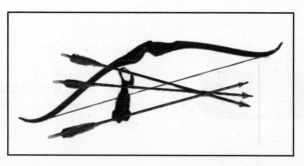

Recurve bows can silently launch modified arrows to create a distraction. Distractions can effectively clear Zombies from an entrance without drawing attention to yourself.

- Consider the use of subordinate reconnaissance missions to determine or confirm mission-specific details.
- Determine alternate routes in case of Zombie attacks.
- Predetermine the number of Zombies the group is willing to defend itself against.
- Determine what actions you will take if you come into contact with Zombies.
- Establish hand signals, and make sure all members of the mission team understand them.
- If your mission is roundtrip, estimate the time of return and a plan for re-entry.
- Communicate with neighbors who may be able to assist the mission or those who are in need of specific supplies or medicines, giving you the opportunity to help them.

See **CHAPTER 10: COMMUNICATION** for information regarding sign kits.

See **APPENDIX A: DISTRACTIONS** for information regarding distractions and ammunition enhanced arrows.

Your kit should be small enough to fit in a belt pack and light enough not to impede movement.

SUPERVISE PREPARATIONS

Before the team departs on a mission, the leader should ensure that everybody has what is required and is well informed about their roles.

PLANNING A MISSION

15-5 MISSION PLANNING, INDIVIDUAL

After the leader has established the plan, the team must prepare both physically and mentally. The members should mentally rehearse and visualize themselves in the field while they work out and improve their fitness in preparation for the mission. Team members with watches should synchronize them with the group leader's. If anybody is unsure or confused about any part of the plan, he or she should discuss it with the group leader. Each member of the mission team is personally responsible for the following:

GENERAL KNOWLEDGE
- Mission purpose
- The duties of group members (or teams)
- Estimated time of departure and return
- Movement procedure
- Alternative routes
- Pre-arranged communication signals
- First-aid

PERSONAL ROLE
- Actions on Zombie contact
- Actions at rest
- Actions at the objective

EQUIPMENT
- Kit
- Food and water
- Weapons and ammunition
- Mission-specific equipment

PLANNING A MISSION

15-6 AFTER-ACTION REVIEW

Each mission is an opportunity to learn and improve. After the mission is completed, realistically review the results. Ask yourself what went right and what needed improvement. Every group has a different dynamic. Discard what does not work and retain what does. Update your maps with current information.

Leaders should make notes in a log after missions are completed, including Zombie counts, the location and disposition of other survivor groups, and possible locations of resources.

Summary

Proper planning is essential to the success of your mission. Have a clear, defined goal. Begin with the end in mind. Make a map. Look for opportunities and areas to avoid. Find the best possible route. Plan for contingencies. Plan individually and as a team.

plan for contingencies

Zombies can get stuck at your door or window or roam in your surrounding area for weeks on end. In general, the best strategy for making a safe exit is to wait them out. However, this luxury might not be an option. Fortunately there are proven strategies for making hostile exits less dangerous.

16–1 INTRODUCTION

If you have Zombies stuck at your door or window, they may be trying to get at a poster or photograph of a human they see inside. Remove all images of humans, even small ones. Blind the doors and windows. Wait another day. If you have fewer than three Zombies in your area, consider exiting through a window or door on a side of your home that is not blocked by Zombies.

There have been reports of survivors being attacked while attempting to navigate through windows and shrubs.

ELEVATED EXITS

It is possible to exit through a second-story window or off a rooftop using a length of rope strong enough to support your weight. You may wish to tie knots every 12 to 18 inches to make the rope easier to hold and climb down.

CHAPTER 16
EXIT STRATEGY

If you need to escape from a window, be sure your anchor
point is strong and stable enough to hold your weight.
Plumbing fixtures, radiators, and wall studs are ideal. If
you must use a piece of furniture, slide it as close to the
window as possible and be aware that it may shift when
you put weight on the rope. Do not use furniture that is
smaller than the window opening.

If your rope is too short, hang from the end and drop,
keeping your feet and knees together, knees slightly bent,
and your chin against your chest.

After you and your group have reached the ground, you'll
have to leave the rope behind and look for a new piece to
replenish your kit.

OTHER SOLUTIONS
There are three known methods for effectively clearing or
concentrating Zombies in your area. Each has advantages
and risks and is useful for specific circumstances. Study
the solutions carefully. Methods include:

1) Pulling a Zombie that's blocking your exit into your
   home and locking it in a room.
2) Directing Zombies in the area to the rear of your home.
3) Eliminating Zombies that are blocking the exit.

CHAPTER 16
EXIT STRATEGY

16–2 PULL & LOCK

If you have only one Zombie stuck at your exit and no other Zombies in the immediate area, this tactic may be your best option. It is relatively quiet, uses no ammunition, and does not require you to destroy the brain. It can be employed without weapons of any kind, although weapons are recommended. It is best performed by three people but can accomplished by one person if he or she is decidedly stronger than the offending Zombie. Take note of the Zombie's stage of decomposition. If it is a fresh Zombie, wait until it is disadvantaged by the full effects of rigor mortis before attempting this tactic.

TEAM ROLES

One person is the "Rabbit," who leads the Zombie to the holding room and therefore must be able to run faster than the Zombie. The other people are "Pushers," who shove the Zombie into the holding room. Collectively, the Pushers must be bigger and stronger than the Zombie. Both the Rabbit and the Pushers must wear protective clothing or armor to prevent bites.

CHOOSING THE HOLDING ROOM

Rooms that lock from the inside are ideal; a Zombie is not smart enough to unlock a door. If you do not have a room that you can easily lock, you will need to nail the door shut after the Zombie has been pushed into the room.

PREPARING THE HOLDING ROOM

Lock or barricade and blind all doors and windows to the room except for the entry point. Set up tripwires near the entry point.

Shields can be very valuable for managing a Zombie attack.

EXECUTION

The Rabbit attracts and leads the Zombie to the holding room. Just past the entry point, the Rabbit stops, turns, and holds its ground. The Pushers join the Rabbit to force the Zombie into the holding room, creating separation from the Zombie by forcibly knocking it down and into the holding room. Consider the following:

- A yoke is ideal for pushing and controlling a Zombie while keeping it at a safe distance.
- Shields put a barrier between you and a Zombie. Use them in the same way riot police use shields for crowd control. Shields can be fashioned out of end tables, coffee tables, trashcan lids, or even cabinet doors. (Add handles to the shields, if possible.)
- Trip wires aid in creating separation.

A lipstick can be used to mark rooms containing Zombies.

SECURING THE ZOMBIE

After successfully pushing the Zombie into the room, lock or nail the entry-point door shut. Then, using large letters, clearly mark the door with a warning: "ALERT! Zombie Inside!"

CHAPTER 16
EXIT STRATEGY

16–3 DIRECTING ZOMBIES

Distractions can be used to draw Zombies away from your preferred exit to an area where they will not be able to see you embark on your mission.

A laser pointer can be used to draw a Zombie's attention.

SECOND STORY

You can call out to Zombies relatively safely from second-story windows. If you have a Zombie at your front door and have access to a second story with windows on all sides, you can usually guide the Zombie to the back of your house by calling out to it. You may have to start at a window on the side of the house to draw the Zombie to the side and then move to a rear window to draw the Zombie to the back of the house.

Take care not draw the attention of more than three Zombies. Zombie hordes are lethal.

BARRICADING

If you have a team capable of barricading a window efficiently while under duress, it should be possible for them to barricade a window even while being attacked by Zombies. The act of barricading a window will draw Zombies to your location. Only consider barricading a window as a means to clear your door if you have the strength and skill to match the Zombies outside.

CHAPTER 16
EXIT STRATEGY

Barricading has been reported with favorably mixed results. There is a possibility that you will draw more Zombies than anticipated.

Rooms that only have one window to the outside are ideal for barricading. They have built-in redundancy. If Zombies manage to push their way into your home, you can exit the room and lock the door behind you, effectively keeping the Zombie(s) outside your perimeter.

Make sure adjacent windows are either barricaded or lead to locked rooms.

See **CHAPTER 8: HOME DEFENSE** for more information regarding the proper procedure for barricading a window.

DRAWING TO A BARRICADED LOCATION

If your home is barricaded, you can use your existing barricades to draw Zombies away from your exit. A whistle will make Zombies aware of your presence and alert other survivors that you are human. The whistle's volume can be adjusted with your breath. Consider using the opportunity to verbally communicate with your neighbors or to simply let off some steam.

Fear the Zombie horde.

REMOTE DISTRACTIONS

Remote distractions draw Zombies to a specific location. For example you can create a remote distraction by throwing a rock near an idle Zombie. If you did not alert the Zombie to your presence, and there are no other distractions, the Zombie may investigate the area where the rock landed for hours or even days.

The following techniques have been reported to effectively distract Zombies:

• Producing flashes and streaks of light with a laser pointer
• Using a remote-controlled car
• Launching hot dogs upwind of offending Zombies. (Some time may need to pass before Zombies become aware of the scent.)
• Playing prerecorded human voices and laughter
• Throwing or waving glow sticks

Drawing Zombies to your home is the most dangerous type of exit strategy.

16–4 ELIMINATION STRATEGIES

Eliminating a Zombie that blocks your exit is a service to the community. Silent techniques are recommended.

STAKING TACTICS

If you have two able-bodied survivors and only one Zombie at your door, consider staking the Zombie as a means of elimination. Zombies are singularly minded, and this technique uses that trait against them. If you securely open the door only a few inches, a Zombie will press into the opening (trying to bite you) and will most likely expose its eyes. Staking a Zombie through the eye socket can be done relatively safely if your door is securely set up to open only a few inches. A door with a chain lock is a good start. If you do not have a chain-locked door, the same effect can be created by blocking the door with heavy furniture so it cannot be opened more than a few inches. Make sure the furniture is heavy enough that it will prevent the door from being pushed open by a Zombie at full strength. If the Zombie can fit its arms and hands through the opening, consider hacking them off with a bladed weapon. Always wear eye and mouth protection when hacking off Zombie limbs.

IMPACT AND BLADE TACTICS

Zombies can be eliminated with an impact or blade weapon upon entry. Consider using a yoke, pitchfork or spading fork to control the Zombie while someone else eliminates it. Also consider using a trip wire.

See **CHAPTER 5: OTHER WEAPONRY** for more information on using yokes.

USING FIREARMS

Shooting firearms will draw Zombies to your location and should be done with extreme caution. However, firearms are highly effective Zombie destroyers. There have been reports of neighborhoods being effectively cleared of Zombies by using firearms. If you are confident in your ability and have plenty of ammunition, consider making an attempt to clear your neighborhood of Zombie activity. (See "cover fire" below for techniques.)

Using firearms should be considered only if your home is fully barricaded and very well supplied.

EXIT STRATEGY

16–5 COVER FIRE

Cover fire can be used to assist your exit if three conditions are met: (1) Your home is fully barricaded, (2) at least two members of your team are staying behind, and (3) one person has and is capable with a firearm.

SNIPER

The sniper is a marksman who can effectively eliminate Zombies with a rifle. The sniper can cover the exiting group only as far as the field of vision allows. Elevated positions are generally preferred. The elderly and even sick survivors can be excellent at this task.

When implementing cover fire, store supplies near the sniping position in case of a breach. Have a rope set up for making an emergency exit.

Whistles can be used to alert teammates.

GROUND FLOOR OBSERVER (GFO)

The ground floor observer (GFO) assists the sniper by checking conditions on the ground floor. The GFO does not need a weapon to be useful, but it is recommended that he or she have one anyway. (A pistol is a superb tool for reducing Zombie hordes at choke points.) If you are a GFO, your job is to monitor all barricades and judge their stability during combat. If a barricade is about to be breached, decide whether to retreat to the second floor or attempt to push

EXIT STRATEGY

the Zombies back. If you decide to push them back, alert others in the house by whistling or shouting to inform them you are on the defensive. If you retreat, alert the sniper on your arrival, and either hole up or begin your own exit strategy.

SPOTTER
Spotters do not need to have a weapon to be useful, but are best equipped with a pistol and impact weapon. A spotter assists the sniper by providing additional observation. In the case of experienced shooters, the spotter can also suggest range and wind corrections. Consider using binoculars.

Summary

Exiting your home when Zombies are present can be simple or very complex, depending on the conditions on the ground. If a Zombie cannot be avoided, consider moving it out of the way of your path by using distractions or pulling it into your home and locking it in a room. If you have the means and confidence, consider eliminating the Zombies. If the situation presents itself, consider adding fire support to a mission.

safety is a force multiplier

CHAPTER 17
VEHICLES

Vehicles provide protection, increase your range, and are recommended even for very short missions. Methods exist for acquiring gasoline. When operating a vehicle, assume that some streets may not be passable. Vehicles can be used as weapons to eliminate Zombies but can also fail or break down. Plan for contingencies.

17-1 GENERAL CONSIDERATIONS

Evaluate the condition of any vehicle before using it. If the vehicle's condition is suspect, weigh the risk of using it. A breakdown in Zombie territory could be catastrophic. Driving in urban areas is more dangerous than rural areas. Abandoned cars and accidents can make streets impassable. Heavy-duty, 4WD vehicles with high clearance are ideal for maneuvering around and pushing through obstacles. When driving, wear your seat belt, adjust your mirrors, and keep your windshield washer fluid topped off. Allow yourself plenty of fuel to get back home. Do not rely on being able to scrounge fuel.

17-2 WHO SHOULD DRIVE?

All drivers need to be able to drive backward at fairly high speed. Ideally drivers should be able to perform the following 180 degree turns:

- Bootlegger's turn. When driving forward, if you have a lever operated emergency brake, turn the wheels sharply and wrench forcibly upward with the brake.
- While driving backward as fast as possible, suddenly and sharply turn the wheels while simultaneously letting off the gas.

17–3 PREPARATIONS

VEHICLE MODIFICATIONS

- Reposition the spare tire and jack for easy access, and practice using the jack before you actually need to.
- Tape your light switches off so you don't accidentally turn them on.
- Disable dashboard lights or set them to the lowest intensity. Disable the dome light, brake lights, reverse lights, and license plate lights.
- Remove any trim and the antenna.
- Secure the hood with a loop of rope or wire to prevent impacts from jarring the hood open.
- Grease the hood, roof, and trunk with petroleum jelly, baby oil, cooking oil, or hand lotion to make it harder for Zombies to cling to your vehicle.
- Keep door hinges greased or oiled to prevent squeaks and groans.

WHAT TO TAKE

- Your kit
- Weapons
- Fire extinguisher
- Blanket to use as a last resort in a Zombie attack

CHAPTER 17
VEHICLES

17–4 TYPES OF VEHICLES
COMMON VEHICLES

• **Motorcycles**
BENEFITS: fast, extremely fuel efficient, easy to navigate around obstacles
DRAWBACKS: riders are exposed

• **Front-Wheel-Drive Cars**
BENEFITS: fuel efficient
DRAWBACKS: exposed drive shaft, low ground clearance

• **Four-Wheel-Drive Cars**
BENEFITS: relatively fuel efficient, more terrain choices
DRAWBACKS: exposed drive shaft, relatively low ground clearance

• **Vans**
BENEFITS: storage space, sturdy construction
DRAWBACKS: exposed drive shaft, relatively inefficient on fuel, poor maneuverability

• **4WD Trucks and SUVs**
BENEFITS: raised body, drive shaft is heavy and designed for rough duty, more terrain choices, storage space, sturdy construction
DRAWBACKS: relatively inefficient on fuel

VEHICLES

SURVIVAL VEHICLE LAND ROVER

The Land Rover Defender is an expedition grade 4x4. The short wheelbase is capable of accomplishing gradients upward of 45 degrees. It has a 1-tonne payload combined with thrifty fuel consumption and excellent clearance.

- **Motor Homes**

BENEFITS: living space, storage space, gas stove, sturdy construction

DRAWBACKS: exposed drive shaft, extremely inefficient on fuel, difficult to maneuver

PICK-UP TRUCKS

Trucks with open beds present increased opportunities to eliminate Zombies while on the move. Using firearms in such circumstances is still dangerous but not as dangerous as on foot because of the speed with which you move away from your firing position. If smashing Zombies from a truck, use impact weapons. Spiked or bladed weapons may hang up in a Zombie and jerk you out of the truck. Do not tether the weapon to yourself.

SPECIALTY VEHICLES

Bulldozers or other heavy construction equipment can be used to destroy Zombies but require specific skill and circumstances.

17–5 FUEL & REFUELING

The easiest way to get gas in this difficult environment is to take it from unclaimed or crashed cars. Do not take gas from a car that has an owner or you may be attacked

CHAPTER 17
VEHICLES

SURVIVAL VEHICLE RV

Although motor homes provide room for supplies, have stoves for cooking, and usually have a rooftop exit, their inability to maneuver severely limits them. If you have no better option, be sure to stock extra gas.

by an angry survivor! Stay away from purposefully parked cars that are locked or modified in any way. As a point of ethics, mark vehicles that you have siphoned fuel from so other survivors don't waste time or take unnecessary risks. A stick or rag in the fuel filler hole indicates an emptied tank. At the very least, leave the fuel filler door open. Do not be tempted to use diesel fuel in your gasoline vehicle; it will not work and will damage your engine beyond repair.

SIPHONING GAS

To siphon gasoline, you will need a long hose or tube that's thin enough to bypass the unleaded-fuel-only restriction and a container for storing the gas. Insert the tubing in the tank as far as it will go. Suck on the tube to draw gasoline out of the tank, being very careful to not swallow or aspirate the gas. (If you get gas in your mouth, spit it out and rinse your mouth with water. Mouthwash or gum may help remove any unpleasant taste.) Once the gas begins to flow, hold the end of the tubing below the lowest part of the gas tank and fill the container. If possible have someone stand look out. Practice this skill in a safe area before performing it in the field.

PIERCING THE GAS TANK

Some vehicles fuel filler pipes are too curved to allow

siphoning. In this case, consider piercing the gas tank with a screwdriver and a hammer. Plastic gas tanks can be pierced with a sturdy knife. Use common sense and take precautions. If possible, have a fire extinguisher nearby, preferably in the hands of your lookout.

You will need two pans for catching the gas once the tank is pierced. They should be wide enough to catch all the gas that spills out and shallow enough to fit underneath the vehicle. Baking pans can be ideal. When one is full, switch to the other and transfer the full pan to your vehicle or to storage. Repeat this process until the tank is empty.

TRANSFERRING GAS
Use a funnel to transfer gas from the container to your vehicle. A funnel can be improvised with a piece of flexible plastic or metal—or a broad range of materials. Be creative. You may have to hold or prop open the unleaded-fuel restriction device in the filler neck.

STORING GAS
Store gasoline in tightly closed containers. Leave a small amount of room in the container to allow for expansion. Store fuel in a cool place away from sources of ignition.

GAS STATIONS
The underground fuel tanks at gas stations can be tapped by people who are trained in the use of the necessary pumping equipment. It is beyond the scope of this manual to teach proper techniques for liberating gasoline from secured underground storage vessels.

A plow is very effective at keeping Zombies from damaging your vehicle.

17–6 DRIVING OFFENSIVELY

SMASHING HEADS

Impact weapons are ideal for re-killing Zombies from a moving vehicle. The vehicle's power adds to the destructive force of the weapon. A good driver should be able to maneuver close enough to the Zombie so the passenger can club it in the head with a baseball bat or similar impact weapon.

RAMMING ZOMBIES

Using your vehicle to ram Zombies is a viable method of elimination, but beware of the tendency for impacted Zombies to be flung up onto the hood and windshield of your vehicle. (This effect is most pronounced in vehicles that have a point of impact below the center of gravity of the average Zombie.) Consider armoring and reinforcing your windshield. Although glass windshields are fairly strong, the impact of a human skull will crack them. The effect is reduced in vehicles with vertical grilles, such as vans and pick-up trucks.

SURVIVAL VEHICLE BULLDOZER

Heavy equipment can be very effective at eliminating Zombies. Raised cockpits make them relatively safe, and the nature of their purpose can be used to incapacitate or crush Zombies.

VEHICLES

ATTACHED ZOMBIES

Zombies may be crushed or broken apart but not eliminated by vehicle impact. This does not reduce the threat of a bite. If the torso of a Zombie is separated by impact, it is likely that the dangerous part, the head and mouth, and a means of locomotion, the arms, will be on your vehicle and remain a threat. You will need to remove the Zombie from the vehicle. If it is clinging to the grille, crush the Zombie against a solid object, such as a wall. If it latches onto the hood, roof, or deck lid, brake forcefully to throw the Zombie off your vehicle. If it latches onto the side, scrape it off on a nearby wall or another car.

It is not "cool" to drive around with Zombies on your vehicle. It is a mark of a novice.

Rubber boots are handy when cleaning up Zombie fluids.

PARKING AND CLEANUP

Before parking, ensure you have not brought any Zombies with you. Always clear your vehicle to ensure there are no Zombies clinging to the undercarriage of your vehicle. Always exit your vehicle under a heightened state of awareness.

When cleaning Zombie remnants, wear gloves. Handle broken glass or jagged sheet metal covered with Zombie fluids with the utmost care. Rinse areas that have been exposed to Zombie fluids with bleach, paying attention to areas that are often touched or used, such as door handles. Bleach must dwell on a surface for at least 10 minutes before it's properly disinfected.

CHAPTER 17
VEHICLES

17-7 BREAKDOWNS IN ZOMBIE COUNTRY

If your vehicle breaks down in Zombie country, exit your vehicle and quickly establish a secure position in the most tactically advantageous place you can. Revise your plan.

- If there are only a few Zombies near your vehicle when it breaks down, strongly consider eliminating them and exiting your vehicle.
- If there are too many Zombies to eliminate, cover yourself with a blanket and try to remain calm. The Zombies may eventually become distracted by other events if they cannot see you or see movement beneath the blanket. This will work only if your windows are intact and closed.

See **CHAPTER 21: ETHICS & BARTER** for more information on seeking refuge.

17-8 DRIVING AT NIGHT

It has been reported that Zombies can be blinded at night with the use of powerful lights. Consider flashing your high beams and maneuvering around Zombies when appropriate.

17-9 VEHICLE REPAIR & MAINTENANCE

It is beyond the scope of this guide to teach vehicle repair. Do your best to maintain your vehicle and keep the radiator free of debris such as leaves, trash, bits of flesh, and clothing. Check your oil and other fluids. The owner's manual should provide instruction on the particulars. Keep tires inflated; slightly lower tire pressures provide

Have a kit for your car too.

increased traction. For long-distance travel, slightly higher pressures result in better fuel economy.

17–10 ADVANCED MODIFICATIONS

It is recommended that you make modifications to your vehicle to increase its effectiveness and safety. Use available skills, tools, and your imagination to armor vulnerable areas. When making modifications, avoid using spikes or other similar projections that might hang up on Zombies, causing them to become stuck to your vehicle.

Common modifications include:

• Armoring and reinforcing your windshield with rebar, chicken wire, plastic cyclone fence, or chain-link fencing.
• Armoring the radiator to prevent punctures by bones and debris.
• Fabricating a hinged hatch in the roof to create an additional route for escape or ingress.

17–11 HITCHHIKING

Hitchhiking, although not ideal, is perfectly acceptable if you find yourself in a desperate situation. Make a large sign clearly marked with your planned destination and hold it over your head so people driving by will not mistake you for a Zombie.

Carjacking is not an acceptable method of gaining access to a vehicle.

17–12 BICYCLES & SKATEBOARDS

BICYCLES

Bicycles have advantages and disadvantages. Most bikes can be operated faster than Zombies can run, but they are highly visible, and it is very difficult to successfully navigate around Zombies running straight at you— especially if Zombies are chasing you from behind.

Riding a bicycle in Zombie country is dangerous and not recommended.

You may be able to use a bicycle to make a quick dash down the street to a neighbor's house. Consider the circumstances on the ground.

SKATEBOARDS

Skateboards can be used to save energy and gain speed when going downhill, but they are loud, can be unstable, and require skill. There have not been any reports of survivors successfully using skateboards to escape Zombies. It may be possible to use skateboards to help transport supplies.

CHAPTER 17
VEHICLES

Summary

If you are a skilled driver and have access to a vehicle, you are in luck. Using a vehicle is the preferred method of transport for most missions. Before going on a mission, you must first modify the vehicle. Being able to safely push through groups of Zombies is a valuable survival skill. High clearance is ideal. Take trips that are well within your range. Although fuel can be foraged along the way, this method should not be relied on. Zombies can be picked off with firearms along the way. Motorized vehicles generate electricity, so check the radio periodically while traveling for the forthcoming government broadcast. Government statements will be broadcast intermittently. After missions are accomplished, be sure to bleach any sensitive areas covered in Zombie fluids and check your oil.

your ability to relax under stress is a force multiplier

CHAPTER 18
ON FOOT

Venturing out on foot in a world plagued with Zombies is inherently dangerous. You must carry weapons and use them as necessary. Create a plan of action in the event you come in contact with Zombies. Adapt to circumstances on the ground. Consider taking woodland or subterranean routes. Consider using mouse holes or bridging buildings in urban areas. Do not be afraid to take detours to remain quietly out of view. Use your experience and imagination to find alternative routes.

18–1 MOVEMENT PROCEDURE

There are three movement procedures: bounding overwatch, group, and column.

BOUNDING OVERWATCH

Bounding overwatch (also known as "leapfrogging") should be used when Zombie contact is highly probable. Divide the group into two teams. For illustration purposes, we will call the groups Alpha Team (AT) and Bravo Team (BT). (You may name your teams, but this is not necessary.) AT moves forward and takes a position that allows them control of the surrounding area. Once they determine the area is safe, they signal BT to advance.

ON FOOT

AT provides support and cover for the advance of BT, which leapfrogs AT and secures a controlling position. (The bounding team must not advance beyond the effective range of the overwatching team's weapons.) This procedure is repeated until the destination is reached or a change in formation is required.

Movement by overwatch is safe but slow; if speed is required, move as a group or in column formation.

GROUP
When crossing large open spaces, such as streets, fields, and bridges, move together in one group. Moving through open spaces as a group will increase efficiency and allow the group to fight or flee as one cohesive unit. Position the leader in the middle so he or she can exert control more easily, and designate a specific team member(s) to provide security to the rear.

The point person should be armed with a semi-automatic pistol and an impact or blade weapon.

Team members should relay information to one another and ensure that everybody is up to speed.

COLUMN
In the case of long, narrow hallways, alleys, or subterranean routes, the team should move in a column (single file) formation. The person who leads the formation is considered "on

point." The point person of a column formation should be the fastest and strongest member of the group and, ideally, armed and proficient with a pistol and an impact weapon (but any firearm will suffice). The group leader should be positioned near the front of the column to control the group's direction. Archers, if present, should be in the middle of the column. The last team member is responsible for security to the rear.

If the team member on point becomes mentally fatigued, consider switching duties.

18–2 RALLY POINTS

Rally points are predetermined meeting areas in case group members become separated due to Zombie contact. Leaders pick rally points along the way, and the information is passed along until all members are aware of them. The position of, number of, and distance between rally points are determined by the tactical situation.

18–3 ZOMBIE INDICATORS

- Some Zombies moan unintelligibly; listen for them.
- Crows and vultures often indicate the presence of Zombies.
- Gunshots attract Zombies. Look toward the opposite direction of the gunshots to spot Zombies that may be in pursuit.
- Disturbed leaves and undergrowth. Zombies move clumsily and will make clear trails.

CHAPTER 18
ON FOOT

18–4 STEALTH, CAMOUFLAGE, MANEUVERS

- Slow, deliberate movements are less likely to attract Zombies. Your ability to relax in stressful situations is a key to your survival.
- Avoid silhouetting yourself on the tops of hills or buildings. A jumbled background, such as a hedge or other vegetation, will camouflage you better than a flat, unbroken expanse, such as a wall or other solid barrier.
- Consider ditches or low points where you can crawl to avoid visibility.
- Hug walls of buildings.
- Peer around corners.
- Step over basement windows.

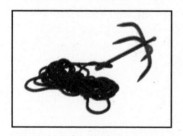

Grappling hooks are an ideal portable escape solution.

- Duck under first-floor windows.

MANEUVERS

- When crossing over walls, make a quick scan of what is on the other side before committing yourself to the ground.
- Use distractions to move Zombies out of the way along your route.

18–5 REST STOPS

If the group becomes fatigued, rest in secluded areas that have multiple routes for escape. If possible, choose an elevated location. Consider the following:

CHAPTER 18
ON FOOT

Hot drinks or soup can boost morale.

- Remain quiet and listen for Zombie moaning.
- Members should alternate between standing watch and eating or maintaining equipment.
- Warm food and drink is a great morale booster, but the smell of cooking food can attract Zombies.
- Be aware that prevailing winds may betray your location; use a handful of dust or grass to determine the wind's direction Extra vigilance must be directed to areas downwind of your position.
- When resting for a long periods, improve the position with obstacles and barricades.
- It may be beneficial to send scouts on reconnaissance missions to gather local supplies.

18–6 ZOMBIE ATTACKS

When Zombies attack, the leader must decide whether to fight or flee, which is often a gut reaction. Prepare for an attack by visualizing and rehearsing different scenarios in your mind before embarking on the mission.

FIGHT
- Eliminate the freshest Zombies first as they pose the greatest threat. Generally, you should combine fire on fast Zombies and use individual fire with slower ones.
- If time allows, consider adjusting your position in order

ON FOOT

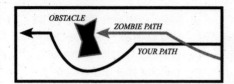

to lead Zombies into naturally occurring obstacles.

- Assist those engaged in hand-to-hand combat only when all other threats are accounted for.

FLIGHT

When fleeing Zombies, the goal is for the entire unit to get out of sight of the Zombie threat as soon as possible. Consider leading the Zombies into naturally occurring obstacles. If you are encumbered by supplies, it may be in your interest to ditch them. Zombies are uninterested in your belongings, and you may be able to retrieve them at a later date.

Distractions are not helpful during a retreat.

Once Zombies lose sight of you, they will not immediately stop chasing you, but they will trail off and lose interest over a period of time. Redundancy is key. Make at least one more turn before resting.

LEAD-AWAYS

A lead-away is a noble and viable strategy if you have slow-moving members in your group (e.g., children or the elderly). This tactic involves one person who takes responsibility for the safety of the entire group by luring

A wheel barrow can be used to transport wounded group members.

the Zombies away from the group. This decision should be discussed before the group goes on a mission. The person performing the lead-away should call out the location he or she will attempt to reach to attain safety. When feasible, the group should devise a plan to rescue the lead-away person if it becomes necessary.

18–7 INJURIES

If you are injured, notify someone immediately. If you can move, begin seeking the closest and safest area to address the problem. Have teammates inform the entire group, if necessary. If you cannot move, inform your teammates of your condition and devise a plan based on conditions on the ground. Consider seeking refuge if conditions permit.

See **CHAPTER 21: ETHICS & BARTER** for more information on seeking refuge.

Gas masks provide protection from both noxious gases and blood splatter. They will NOT help you in an oxygen-deficient atmosphere.

18–8 SUBTERRANEAN

ON FOOT

ROUTES

Most underground passages are Zombie free, but this

Earplugs are essential for preserving your hearing when using firearms, especially in tight quarters.

generalization cannot be counted on. When traveling underground, use the column formation. The point person should be the strongest member of your group, preferably armed with a pistol and flashlight. There should be a distance of approximately 10 yards between each person in the group. The last person is in charge of marking the route with chalk or paint.

Headlamps provide hands-free illumination.

PREPARATION

- Check the weather. Avoid storm drains if rain is a possibility.
- Everyone should wear earplugs. The sound of gunshots can destroy your eardrums. Rely on your vision.
- Dress for slippery passages. Wear boots with good traction; wrap them with chicken wire or screen wire, if available.
- Each person should have a flashlight, if available.
- The leader should carry a map, a rope, a compass, and a note pad, if available.

ENTERING

Use a crowbar to open manholes. The point person should secure the underground passage before the rest of the team enters. Once underground, close the manhole and wait approximately 10 minutes to acclimate before moving. Headache, nausea, and drowsiness may indicate the presence of a life-threatening atmosphere. (Some lethal gases are odorless or dull the sense of smell, masking their presence.) If anyone in the group experiences any of these symptoms at any point, the plan should be aborted, and the team should exit the underground passageway as quickly as possible.

POINT PERSON RESPONSIBILITY

- Keep the pace slow and cautious.
- Pause approximately every 50 yards to check for changes in your physical condition and the safety of the location. Remove your earplugs and listen for signs of Zombies or other threats.

- Keep a rope attached to a sturdy belt or harness. If someone falls unconscious, the rope can be used to extricate the person so CPR can be started.

LEADER RESPONSIBILITY

When a route to the surface is discovered, the leader should investigate it, try to determine the location, and note the Zombie presence. Use the note pad to draw the route as it unfolds. (Update maps with these sketches.)

Carabiners can add redundancy and safety to your bridges.

18–9 BRIDGING BUILDINGS

If you need to cross a gap between two buildings, you can do so by building a bridge from rooftop to rooftop out of ladders or planks of wood. If you intend to bridge a gap between buildings, keep the following rules of thumb in mind:

- When connecting two ladders, there must be an overlap. Splint the joint of the ladders with a strong piece of wood or metal. Duct tape or rope can be used to couple the ladders.
- Attach a length of cord or rope to the far end of the ladder to help you position it, especially over particularly wide gaps. The person holding the the rope should be elevated as much as possible to have as much control in positioning the ladder as possible.
- If you plan on constructing bridges from materials removed from the inside of the building, such as studs and joists, orient the widest portion of the studs vertically to provide the most strength and rigidity.
- Screws and nails can be reclaimed from interior construction (do not overlook those used to secure the drywall to the studs). In a pinch, wiring and furnishings, such as strips of upholstery, curtains, drapes, or clothing, can be used. Be creative and resourceful.
- In practice, only one person should cross a bridge at one time. If possible, an accomplished marksman should provide cover for those crossing the bridge.
- When crossing gaps with improvised bridges, add a safety line of rope above and parallel to the bridge that people can hang onto or clip themselves to. The rope

can be secured to internal structures, such as plumbing or wall studs. (Care must be taken to protect the rope from sharp edges and chafing.) A carabiner or quick link, such as the type that would be used to join two lengths of chain, can be used to attach a makeshift harness to the safety line. The harness can be improvised out of rope (e.g., a Swiss seat), or you may already have a commercial harness, such as the kinds used for hunting tree stands or industrial safety.

18–10 MOUSE HOLES

A mouse hole is an opening about two feet in diameter that is created by smashing through or cutting into a wall or floor. Mouse holes can be created between adjoining rooms (whether side by side or one on top of the other) or buildings. Dangerous sections of large buildings can be bypassed entirely by using mouse holes. (However, some modern buildings have cement floors between levels.) If the electricity in your area is still operational, be mindful of hidden wiring to avoid being shocked. A sledgehammer, wood-splitting maul, or axe are invaluable for opening mouse holes between buildings.

18–11 IN FIELD OPPORTUNITY

There is an opportunity to eradicate Zombies using a chain-link fence if you have and are skilled with stake weapons. If you are on one side of a chain-link fence and Zombies are on the other side, the Zombies are very susceptible to stake attacks. Simply call them to the fence and re-kill them with stake weapons. Zombie eradication is a service to your community.

See **CHAPTER 5: OTHER WEAPONRY** for more information on using stake weapons.

18-12 ENTERING & CLEARING BUILDINGS

Before entering a building, do your best to determine whether it is vacant. Vacant buildings usually have broken windows or open doors. Locked doors usually mean the building is inhabited. If you aren't sure, knock before entering the building. If it is vacant, shotguns or pistols combined with impact weapons are recommended for clearing the building.

STRATEGY

- Listen for Zombies periodically. Some Zombies are "talkative" and will never stop making noise.
- Enter a building one person at a time. The point person should secure the first room before the group enters.
- Leave the door slightly ajar until you determine whether the building is safe.
- Be extremely quiet.
- Carefully inspect each room as a group. If you discover a Zombie inside a room, consider closing the door and locking it in the room. Always mark rooms that contain trapped Zombies.

See **CHAPTER 21: ETHICS & BARTER** for information on entering a home known to be inhabited by strangers.

Summary

Traveling on foot in Zombie country is a scary proposition. However, there are many opportunities that can make your

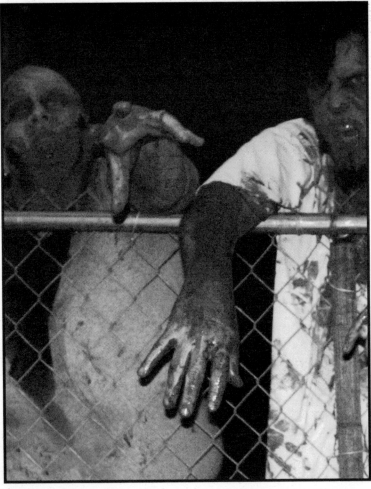

Zombies always take a direct route toward their target. Fences are ideal barriers. These survivors were calm enough to take pictures before eliminating the Zombies stuck at this fence.

[Photo courtesy "Saundra's Soldiers"]

proper training & accurate knowledge foster self-confidence

CHAPTER 19
HOT SPOTS

Hot spots are areas of substantial resources with a high potential for Zombies, Zombie hordes, and other survivors. (Grocery stores and camping outfitters are common examples.) Some hot spots may be overwhelmed by Zombie hordes. Some may be in operation as distribution centers or barter businesses. Some may be vacant. Regardless, always use extra caution when approaching a hot spot.

19-1 COMMON HOT SPOTS

GROCERY STORE
- Food and beverages
- Large, flat roof for collecting rain water and for sniping
- Parking lots provide wide field of vision
- Difficult to heat
- Vermin

CAMPING OUTFITTER / FIREARMS STORE
- Weapons
- Archery equipment
- Dehydrated food
- Camping supplies
- Hardware
- Water transport

HOT SPOTS

LIQUOR STORE / BEER DISTRIBUTOR
- Liquor, wine, beer

POLICE STATION
- Weapons
- Holding cells for quarantine rooms
- Emergency electricity
- Could be fortified by local authorities

SHOPPING MALL
- Large variety of supplies
- Many entrances/exits
- Large, flat roof for collecting rain water and sniping
- Large area to maintain control
- Parking lots provide wide field of vision
- Possibly many people in building to feed, manage, and trust
- Difficult to heat

Remove the baskets from ski poles to use them as staking weapons.

RESTAURANT
- Food
- Beverages
- Gas stove
- Vermin

Restaurants can provide opportunities for procuring weaponry.

PHARMACY
- Medical supplies
- Food
- Beverages

CHAPTER 19
HOT SPOTS

GAS STATION / CONVENIENCE STORE
• Gasoline is nearly impossible to obtain without the proper equipment.
• Food
• Beverages

HOSPITAL

Most hospitals have become breeding grounds for the VRV and should be considered EXTREMELY dangerous.

19–2 GENERAL CONSIDERATIONS

Hot spots should be observed before entering. If possible, set up camp nearby to observe the hot spot before attempting to comlete your mission. Notice the following and plan accordingly:

• If the building has been blinded or barricaded, it is highly likely that survivors are inside and have claimed it. Attempt to communicate with the occupants.

• If the building has a breach, such as a broken window, there are probably no survivors inside unless they have yet to repair the breach or have sealed off the breach inside the building. Consider occupying the spot.

• If you observe survivors approaching the building, watch how the situation unfolds. Consider communicating with them or offering assistance.

CHAPTER 19
HOT SPOTS

• If you observe survivors in the building, attempt to communicate with them before entering.

19–3 INHABITED HOT SPOTS

Begin communication by letting the inhabitants know who you are, what you are interested in, and what you have to offer. If they are agreeable, establish protocol for entering the building. They may have a plan in place for bringing in refugees for bartering purposes. If they are not agreeable, move to another hot spot that may have the resources you are looking for. If your survival depends on the resource inside, and there are no other viable options, consider the use of force to get what you need.

See **CHAPTER 21: ETHICS & BARTER** for information on seeking refuge and bartering for goods.

See **CHAPTER 10: COMMUNICATION** for various methods to establish your intentions with other survivors.

ENTRY STRATEGY

Do not use firearms against Zombies in front of buildings containing friendly survivors.

Use distractions to move Zombies away from the building.

See **APPENDIX A: DISTRACTIONS.**

SIGN KIT
Do you have a plan for entry / for exit?

CHAPTER 19
HOT SPOTS

My name is _____
We can't shoot without risking your safety.
<— We will create a distraction over there —>
Can you _____ ?
Thank you!

19–4 UNINHABITED HOT SPOTS

If a hot spot is uninhabited and an has acceptably low Zombie concentration, prepare to enter it. If necessary, use distractions to move Zombies away from the building. Once inside, consider the following:

TAKE WHAT YOU NEED AND MOVE ON

This method is simple, safe, and effective. When combined with a vehicle, this plan is akin to making a trip to the grocery store, but with guns.

Do NOT hoard supplies.

SHORT STAY

Stay until the next group of survivors approaches. When they approach, assist them with entry and make their acquaintance before leaving.

See **CHAPTER 8: HOME DEFENSE** for more information on setting up a quarantine room.

PERMANENT STAY

Many people are simply choosing to remain in hot spots, so communities are forming inside. This is not recommended.

HOT SPOTS

The VRV can spread quickly through crowds. Large groups of people are a liability. There have been reports of Zombie hordes forming in crowded grocery stores within minutes.

SET UP A DISTRIBUTION CENTER

If you have a very strong team capable of fending off repeated Zombie attacks and challenges from other survivors, consider setting up an unoccupied hot spot as a distribution center. A properly run distribution center provides the following services for the community:

• Keeps people from forming crowds
• Evenly allocates resources
• Establishes a hub (consider adding bulletin boards)

Consider the following rules of thumb if you decide to take on the responsibility of running a distribution center:

• Barricade the building. Zombie attacks will occur.
• Plan ways for survivors to safely enter and exit your building.
• Create a quarantine area.
• Make portions per person equal.
• Repeat visits, if allowed, should be moderated.
• Advertise the rules up front and outside.

19–5 TRANSPORTING SUPPLIES

Transporting supplies can be useful when you have specific needs or if you have an abundance of a certain resource that you want to haul to a safer location.

HOT SPOTS

Vehicles are the best way to transport goods, but if you do not have access to a vehicle, it can be done using the following methods:

A heavy pack can be ideal for transporting supplies, but do not hesitate to drop it if attacked.

BACKPACK

A backpack is an excellent way to transport small supplies. Do not overload your pack. Pack a comfortable load—one with which you feel comfortable jogging. Place heavy items on the bottom, but do not bury essential items, such as ammunition or specialized weapons. If you use the waist or sternum strap on a large pack, practice disengaging it for rapid removal in case of Zombie attacks.

BICYCLE

Use a bicycle with panniers or improvised racks to transport supplies in areas with low Zombie densities. Bicycles conserve fuel and can be used to move supplies more efficiently than you can on foot. Bicycle wheels can also be used to build makeshift carts.

WHEELBARROW

A wheelbarrow is convenient for transporting bulky or heavy items over short distances. Wheelbarrows or carts with large pneumatic (air-filled) tires are best for use over rough terrain. Rubber pads can be added to the support legs of wheelbarrows to reduce noise.

Shopping carts work best on smooth surfaces.

CARTS

Shopping carts should be avoided, if possible, because they have small wheels that limit the terrain on which they are effective. A shopping cart is also relatively noisy, and its inevitable wobbling wheel will undoubtedly exacerbate an already stressful situation.

Summary

Different types of hot spots provide different opportunities. Plan carefully when attempting to gather resources from a hot spot. If possible, move to a location from which you can observe the area before entering it. If a hot spot is occupied by survivors, communicate with them. If it is not, enter and, if possible, secure the premises. Consider taking what you need and moving on, staying until the next group arrives, or setting up a distribution center. Do not allow large groups of people to form at hot spots because the VRV preys on crowds.

Zombies are attracted to hot spots and will form hordes. Hordes have a greater combined strength and can break windows that otherwise afford good protection. The combined strength of these Zombies broke the window of this retail store.

[Photo found in camera]

be willing to take detours

CHAPTER 20
ZOMBIE HUNTING

Eradication of the Zombie menace is a service to the community if it is performed properly. There are currently two accepted methods: Luring and Hunting. Consider your neighbors when performing this noble duty. Do not draw Zombies toward survivors that do not agree with your plans. Reserve bullets for Zombies.

Ammunition and firepower are your greatest assets. If you do not have enough ammunition to clear the surrounding area, your plan may fail. Plan missions around excess.

Twine can be used to create trip obstacles. Trip wires can also alert you of Zombies approaching your area.

20-1 BASE CAMPS

Launch eradication missions from a base camp. Base camps provide a secure position away from your home base to plan, rest, and maintain your equipment. They can be located in remote areas, abandoned neighborhoods, or any place you and your neighbors have agreed to seize the responsibility for a Zombie-free future. Your base camp should be stocked with enough supplies to last at least one week. A base camp in a tall building with good visibility is ideal.

Coffee percolators like this one make it easy to brew fresh coffee over an open fire or camp stove.

WOODLAND BASE CAMPS

Woodland base camps are exposed to attack, but they can be useful for launching missions. Woodland terrain offers several advantages:

- It's often devoid of Zombies.
- It's difficult for Zombies to navigate.
- It's often close to hot spots.
- It provides for camouflage.

When setting up a woodland base camp, consider the following:

- Elevated terrain is an advantage.
- Natural obstacles provide protection against Zombies.
- Trip wires should be set up to provide early warnings.
- Have an exit strategy with at least two options.

See **APPENDIX B: EARLY WARNING** for more information on setting up trip wires and traps that sound alarms.

<u>20–2 LURING</u>

It is possible to lure Zombies to a location where they can be destroyed with relative ease. Zombies can be successfully lured using:

- Vehicles
- Humans
- Distractions
- Discharges from a firearm (consider your ammunition supply)

Good locations for Zombie eradication include:

Recordings of human voices are very effective at drawing Zombies.

- Stadiums
- Fenced-in yards
- Fields
- Deserted neighborhoods
- Dead ends
- Swimming pools
- Parking lots
- Alleyways

See **APPENDIX A: DISTRACTIONS** for more information on what Zombies respond to.

PIED PIPER

This technique uses a fast, fit team member (the Piper) who is intimately familiar with the area to lure Zombies out of hiding along a known route. Teammates must maintain constant visual contact and have a plan in place to assist the Piper if trouble occurs.

Bicycles can be effectively put to use by the pied piper.

ZOMBIE HUNTING

The Piper leads the Zombies to a pre-planned area for eradication. This could be a dead end, a fenced-in yard or even your barricaded base camp. There must always be an exit strategy in place for the Piper. At night, the Piper can carry a glow stick to enhance his or her attraction.

DAMSEL IN DISTRESS

Bullhorns can be used to call Zombies into large holding areas and are found at many stadiums.

This advanced luring method suspends a team member (the Damsel) over an enclosure to lure Zombies into a trap where they can be eradicated. (The Damsel should be volunteer who is lightweight and brave.) The Damsel is secured by a rope harness and suspended by makeshift pulley system, such as a rope draped over a stout tree limb. Be certain that the harness, rope, and tree are strong and secure and that there is an exit strategy for the Damsel before employing this dangerous but effective technique.

There is a report that a motivated band of eradicators in the Baltimore area used this method to eliminate more than 5,000 Zombies in an Olympic-sized swimming pool.

KILL IT WITH FIRE

Combine diesel fuel or oil with a fenced swimming pool, and you'll have an efficient means for mass eradication. This tactic is known as having a "pool party."

Fenced areas have been reported to be problematic for burning Zombies as it is difficult to contain the fire. Eventually the fence weakens and blazing Zombies wander off, starting other fires.

Isolated cement or cinder block buildings also work well as corrals. Consider the following:

• Waste motor oil is an excellent fuel source.
• Ignite the fuel with a flaming arrow or Molotov cocktail.
• Fuel may not ignite or burn well if there are too many Zombies. Do not overfill your corral.
• Adding fuel after the corral is filled with Zombies may result in a more successful burn.
• Those in the immediate area are advised to use respirators to ward off noxious smoke and vapors.

Lanterns can be used to lure Zombies.

LURING AT NIGHT

There is no specific advantage to luring Zombies at night. Zombies do not give off a heat signature to use with thermal-imaging sights. Starlight scopes are effective but not as effective as any scope on a bright sunny day. However, at night you'll have a new range of potential distraction techniques: lights. There have been reports of enterprising Zombie hunters improvising spotlights from motorcycle and car headlights and using them like deer spotters, blinding Zombies with bright lights. Lights can be powered by battery or generator.

CHAPTER 20
ZOMBIE HUNTING

See **APPENDIX A: DISTRACTIONS** for more information on techniques for luring Zombies at night.

20–3 HUNTING

PATROLLING

Patrolling by vehicle is most effective in rural areas with low Zombie concentrations. Slow, methodical vehicle patrols with a driver and at least one gunner are ideal. Each member of the patrol should have a firearm and know how to get back to the secure location in case of a breakdown. Designate rally points along the way.

MUTUAL KILL ZONE (MKZ)

An MKZ requires two teams that work together. The teams establish elevated shooting positions opposite each other at either end of an open space. (Town or city streets are ideal for this method.) The noise from each team's shooting lures Zombies into view for the other team. Keep the firing range under 100 yards to maximize effective hits. Cease shooting an hour or two before your planned exit to allow the Zombie density to taper off to a manageable level.

RING AROUND THE ROSIE

This method is suitable only for the fittest and most motivated teams operating independently. Over the course of many missions, establish a circular route with elevated shooting positions along the way. As your team eliminates Zombies, other Zombies will accumulate at the base of your position. Use your route to then circle around and engage these collected Zombies. Select shooting positions for effective coverage in areas where Zombies gather. Use mouse holes to move through adjacent buildings, and use bridging techniques to overcome wide spans. Multiple entry and exit points allow the most flexibility in planning. Enhance the shooting positions with range cards.

20–4 WINTERTIME

The winter season will present new opportunities for Zombie eradication. Take advantage of periods when the temperature is well below freezing, when Zombies freeze. Frozen Zombies are not dangerous and can be moved into pens. It is possible to saw off their heads during this state, but it takes some time without a chainsaw. You must sever the spine between the first and third cervical vertebrae to effectively kill a Zombie. Otherwise, you may be confronted by a biting head upon thawing. If there is only one Zombie to be eliminated, this may be fine, but if you have many Zombies to eradicate, it is advisable to load them into trucks and place them in fenced or locked areas, where they can be eliminated at a later time.

Summary

Zombie eradication is a service to your community. If you are able bodied and have the means, it is considered your duty as an American citizen. Be considerate of your fellow survivors when eradicating Zombies. Always consider what lays beyond your target. A bright future awaits those who responsibly hasten the restoration of society.

ZOMBIE HUNTING

Burning Zombies can be an effective method of eradication. Make sure that the fire can be contained. This Zombie spread a fire from one building to another, destroying much of Kutztown, Pennsylvania.

[Photo courtesy Mr. Schüdenhofferstein]

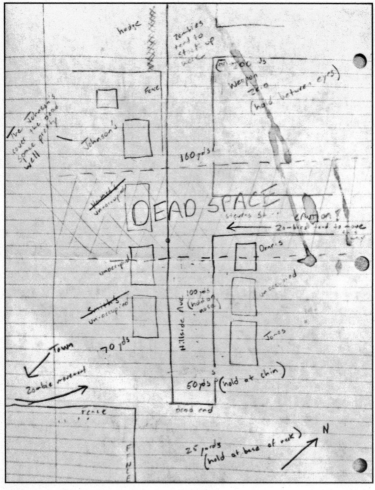

Range Cards: Drawing maps to determine ranges will help with your ability to snipe Zombies from long distances and visualize kill zones.

arrogance leads to blind spots

CHAPTER 21
ETHICS & BARTER

There is more to surviving this threat than simply staying alive. We must share and help one another to retain our basic humanity, teach our children that there is something beyond self-interest, and emerge from this ordeal in a manner that will foster good will in the reconstruction.

21–1 GENERAL CONSIDERATIONS

In this harsh new landscape, the traditional checks to uncivil human behavior are no longer in place. Thankfully, early reports indicate that most survivors are cooperating with one another. Yet there are individuals and groups engaged in unlawful and immoral behavior. These unruly groups are a threat. Law enforcement is in no position to protect you. You are responsible for yourself and your loved ones. You have a responsibility to defend yourself and when doing so must use sound judgment and reason.

21–2 WHAT NOT TO DO

MALINGERING

You are responsible for yourself. You cannot expect to rely on others if you are capable of fending for yourself. If you lack the knowledge or skills required, learn them. Your will to live and an open mind are the most valuable things you possess.

CHAPTER 21
ETHICS & BARTER

HOARDING

Hoarding refers to the stockpiling of supplies in excess of group or individual needs. If food is going to waste due to spoilage or if you have a large quantity of ammunition, you should share your good fortune with other survivor groups who are in need.

PROFITEERING

Profiteering refers to demanding exorbitant amounts of trade goods for basic necessities. You can expect to receive compensation for your supplies but only when the exchange is fair. Let your conscience be your guide.

TOLLS AND CHECKPOINTS

Impeding or restricting the travel of survivors for the purposes of obtaining trade goods or services is a crime. Individuals or groups engaging in this practice can expect a justified, hostile response from other survivors.

RUMOR MONGERING

Bad information and rumors skew the decision-making process of other survivors. Do not spread rumors. If something seems too good to be true, it probably is. In addition, if a rumor seems outlandishly bad, it is probably false. Consider what the source may have to gain before accepting information at face value.

These are some of the false rumors that are circulating at the time of this writing:

• There is a cure for the VRV, and someone is selling it.
• Carriers are turning into Zombies.

- There is a cure, but the government is withholding it from the general populace or certain groups.
- Zombies are turning back into humans.
- Zombies are laying eggs.
- There is a Norwegian invasion fleet off of the coast of New Jersey.
- This situation is the result of a powerful satellite broadcast from China (and other ridiculous rumors related to the origin of the outbreak).

21–3 SEEKING REFUGE

When seeking refuge, do not take offense if a homeowner asks you to inspect your hands, arms, or neck for Zombie bites. It is the right of every survival group to ensure their safety. If you are turned away for any reason, do not take it personally. There are many factors that determine whether a group can take on additional members. They are not obligated to give you a reason.

If taken in by fellow survivors, be mindful that they are sharing precious resources and taking a risk by helping you. Be respectful of the beliefs and folkways of other survivors you encounter. One survivor's eccentric behavior is another's coping mechanism. Do not expect anything from your host. Help with chores and other daily tasks, and show your appreciation with gifts whenever possible.

21–4 FORAGING ETHICS

Survivors are generally reliant on food that was packaged before the outbreak, especially in urban environments. Foraging will be necessary before society is restored.

ETHICS & BARTER

When foraging, make every effort not to take food that belongs to the living. Only forage in buildings that show signs of abandonment: unlocked or open doors and broken windows. When gathering fuel from a vehicle, try to make certain the vehicle is not being used by someone. If the vehicle is locked, do not loot it. Plant gardens when and where possible.

Condoms are easy to carry and often have high trade value.

21–5 BARTER

There have been reports of two types of successful barter businesses: supply depots and guide services. Supply depots can be found almost anywhere—from hot spots to well-stocked basements. When making transactions, always strive for a fair deal in which both parties benefit.

ADVERTISING

Advertise the supplies you have for trade as well as the supplies you are looking for. Make signs using markers, pens, paint, or opaque tape and paper or pieces of wood. Hang the signs from a second-story window, if possible. Be creative. Do not use false advertising to lure potential traders.

COMMONLY TRADED ITEMS
• Fresh vegetables
• Fresh meat
• Canned or dehydrated food
• Vitamins
• Ammunition

ETHICS & BARTER

- Bleach
- Condoms (trade value varies)
- Cigarettes
- Painkillers
- Lighters and matches
- Candy

You may be able to trade for enough ammunition to clear your local neighborhood of Zombies.

GUIDE OR TAXI SERVICES

Guiding is the act of escorting other survivors through potentially dangerous territories. Although guiding can be done on foot, it is highly recommended to use a vehicle.

It has been determined that crystals have no effect on Zombie behaviors.

21–6 ZOMBIE RIGHTS ORGANIZATIONS

Zombie Rights Organizations (ZROs or "zeroes") have arisen in this difficult time. The goal of a ZRO is to corral Zombies and keep them safe from harm in the hopes that a cure will be found. Members of these organizations can be identified by the presence of shields and yokes with a conspicuous absence of weapons.

Members of ZROs are driven by passion. Thus, they can be dangerous and should be avoided. However, they must be afforded the same rights as any other person.

CHAPTER 21
ETHICS & BARTER

It has been reported that some groups are attempting to use "Holistic Love" methods to try and return Zombies into productive members of society. Rumors exist that the singing, chanting, and drumming utilized for "treatment" calms Zombies and reverses the course of infection. This theory has been tested and proven false. The odor of incense, sage, patchouli oil, and bleach may reveal the location of such groups. Be aware of their areas of operation and stay away from them.

Corralled Zombies are usually hidden in protected places and tend to stay fresh longer. Their escape would result in a particularly lethal horde.

There have been reports of the potential for a unique viral/fungal comorbidity condition that retards the decomposition of Zombies and may even give them vigor over time. The conditions in which corralled Zombies are confined may be ideal for the spread of this phenomena. Be aware that if you discover corralled Zombies you may be facing a type of Zombie that you have not encountered before.

Known ZROs Include:
- The Zombie Protection Society
- People for the Ethical Treatment of Zombies (PETZ). (This group does not use any kind of firearms or weaponry.)
- Zombies Are Still People (ZASP)

The future is bright.

DEGRADATION OF ZOMBIE TEST SUBJECT

The government has corralled and monitored Zombies since Day 3 of the outbreak. The degrading action of birds and other wildlife has reduced one outdoor test Zombie known as "Harry" quite significantly. Harry has been frozen and thawed several times. Although his animation appears to be never-ending, his movement and coordination have degraded, and he has slowed down. It can be surmised that Harry will be on his knees in just a few months.

Trust science.

Your government is currently accepting mail at:
Bureau of Apocalyptic Events
Northeast Region
P.O. Box 1138
Stroudsburg, PA 18360

Reports are encouraged and will be considered for future publication and/or broadcast.

APPENDIX A
DISTRACTIONS

Zombies are generally curious and predictable. Idle Zombies can be tricked into investigating false leads. This can be especially handy to get Zombies to move out of your way by diverting their attention to some type of distraction. Always consider your neighbors before creating a distraction. Do not draw Zombies to a neighbor's home without the neighbor's consent.

A-1 GENERAL CONSIDERATIONS

Zombies can be distracted by sight, smell, and sound, but nothing works better than a living, breathing human being. The following types of distractions have been reported to work (in order of relative effectiveness):

- Human forms (including mannequins)
- Movement
- Unnatural sounds
- Bright lights
- The smell of hot dogs, bacon, or processed meats

The louder the sound, the more aggressively Zombies will move toward it. Gunshots will generally draw idle Zombies at full speed from up to a mile away. If there is gunfire going off around your location, you may observe a "zigzagging effect," as local Zombies brainlessly move from distraction to distraction.

DISTRACTIONS

LINKING DISTRACTIONS

If you want to move Zombies over long distances, you may need to link your distractions, luring the Zombies from one distraction to another.

A–2 REMOTE DISTRACTIONS

Remote distractions draw Zombies to a remote location; they can be portable and used in the field.

A simple example of creating a remote distraction is throwing a rock near an idle Zombie. If there are no other distractions and you are not spotted in the act, the Zombie may investigate the area where the rock landed for hours or even days, looking for the source of the noise or movement. (be aware that Zombies do not investigate animals or naturally occurring movements, such as leaves blowing in the wind.)

The following techniques have been reported or observed to effectively distract Zombies:

• Fireworks
• Glow sticks
• Laser pointers
• Remote-controlled cars
• Hot dogs (some time may need to pass before Zombies become aware of the scent)
• Fire extinguishers (bind the extinguisher in the "on" position and launch it away from your exit or location)
• Prerecorded human voices and laughter

A–3 SHOTGUN SHELL-ENHANCED ARROW

An effective long-range distraction can be made using a bow as the launching device and an arrow as the vessel for the distraction. This allows for portable, relatively accurate distractions that work especially well in urban environments. With a few simple items and careful work, a shotgun shell-enhanced arrow (SSEA) can be created. The technology utilizes an inertia operated firing pin that slides to the rear of the arrow upon release and slides forward to strike the primer of a shotgun shell upon impact.

MATERIALS REQUIRED
• Aluminum arrow
• Cigarette lighter (or other heat source)
• Pliers
• Steel pin or bolt that fits inside the arrow shaft
• Fine metalworking file
• Cotter pin
• Roll of tape
• Shotgun shell of any gauge
• Aluminum beverage can
• Sharp knife and/or heavy-duty scissors or shears
• Metal straight-edge (ruler)

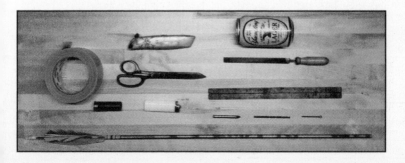

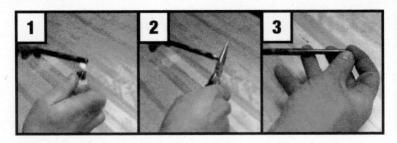

INSTRUCTIONS

Step 1: Heat the shaft of the arrow near the threaded insert to loosen the insert.

Step 2: Use pliers to remove the threaded insert.

Step 3: Check the fit of the firing pin (a metal piece that is filed to a point to engage the shotgun shell). It should fit somewhat snugly in the shaft yet be able to slide freely.

Step 4: Grasp the firing pin with the pliers and sharpen the tip. An included angle of approximately 60 degrees is ideal. Take care to ensure the point is centered with the axis of the pin. A needle-sharp point is NOT desirable; the pin should have a slightly flat tip. File the other end of the pin flat, beveling its edge just slightly. File any burrs or roughness off the length of the pin, if necessary.

Step 5: Approximately eight inches from the open end of the arrow, use the corner of the file to make small holes for the cotter pin on either side of the shaft. Align one of the holes with the different colored feather or vane (nock feather). This will ensure that the cotter pin is more easily removed while nocked. Do not make the holes too big. Use the cotter pin to gauge the correct size. Once you

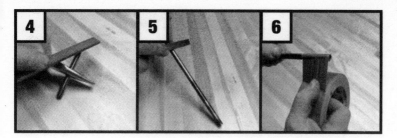

have made small holes, it should be possible to enlarge them to the correct size with a small nail. (A drill with the proper size bit works best if you have electricity.)

Step 6: Carefully and TIGHTLY wrap tape around the open end of the arrow. Ensure that each layer is precisely aligned with the last. Continue to add tape until the tape's diameter is equal to the diameter of the shotgun shell. Any type of tape can be used for this; however, if the width of the tape is less than half the length of the shotgun shell, add a second winding of tape behind the first to account for the discrepancy.

Step 7: Insert the firing pin into the arrow with the tip of the pin pointing toward the open end. Make sure the pin slides freely. (Do not use oil to lubricate the pin because the oil could damage the primer of the shotgun shell.)

Step 8: Allow the firing pin to slide all the way to the back of the arrow. Insert the safety cotter pin through the holes in the shaft and bend one leg. (It is best if the loop of the safety pin is on the same side as the different colored feather or vane.) To test the function of the safety, hold the back of the arrow and swing the tip toward the ground. The safety cotter pin should stop the firing pin from falling

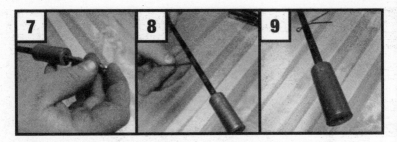

out of the shaft. If it doesn't, you must diagnose the problem and correct it before continuing.

Step 9: The photo shows the correct safety cotter pin configuration. (A short loop of cord can be attached to the cotter pin to aid in its removal.)

Step 10: Any gauge of shotgun shell may be used. A twelve-gauge shell is used here.

Step 11: Carefully file off the rim of the shell's brass head. (If you don't have a file, use any rough, abrasive surface.)

Step 12: Carefully cut the ends off of an aluminum beverage can. (A neat edge is not required at this point.) Try to cut the can at the line where the can bevels toward the top and bottom. Heavy-duty scissors work best, but any type of cutting tool can be used.

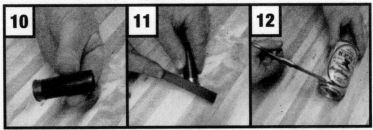

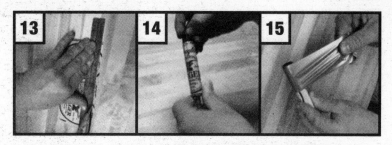

Step 13: Use a metal straight-edge and a sharp knife to make the long sides of the aluminum strip parallel.

Step 14: Place the shotgun shell at the taped end of the arrow, with the brass (primer) end of the shell touching the arrow. TIGHTLY wrap the aluminum strip around the shell and the end of the arrow, ensuring that each layer of the strip is precisely aligned with the last. Continue wrapping the aluminum strip until you have a tight, neat assembly. Ensure that the shell is snug against the arrow.

Step 15: Use tape to secure the aluminum at the front.

Step 16: Use tape to secure the aluminum at the rear.

NOTE: Neat, meticulous work will provide the best chance for success.

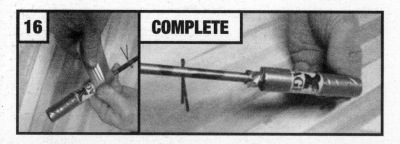

DISTRACTIONS

SAFETY
- The modified arrow must be handled like a firearm. It must never be pointed at anyone or any part of the archer's body.
- The archer should wear eye protection and a heavy glove on his or her bow hand.
- The safety cotter pin must never be removed until the arrow is nocked and pointed at the target.
- When drawing the bow, the arrow must point upward.
- When the arrow is released, the archer must take cover before the arrow makes contact with the target.
- When engaging vertical targets, be aware that the arrow may forcibly fly back at the archer.
- If the arrow is not released for some reason after the safety pin has been removed, the safety pin must be re-inserted immediately.
- If it is not possible to re-insert the safety pin, the arrow must be made safe by bending and breaking the shaft while the firing pin is positioned at the rear of the arrow. (Save the components for later use.)

MODE OF EMPLOYMENT
- This enhanced arrow is intended for use as a distraction only. It is NOT recommended for use as an anti-Zombie munition.
- Shots should be planned so the relation between the arrow and the surface are as perpendicular as possible.
- High lob shots onto a hard surface work best.
- Shots against hard vertical surfaces are acceptable.
- If you retrieve an arrow that did not fire, the firing pin should be allowed to slide fully to the rear of the shaft and the safety pin must be re-inserted.

Zombies have no place in our society

EARLY WARNING

Early warning devices can help secure the perimeter of your location. Because Zombies are oblivious to danger, trip wires do not need to be camouflaged. Trip wires should be clearly visible to humans.

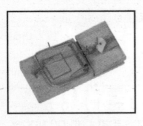

Mousetraps make for handy triggers in creating an early warning device.

B–1 EARLY WARNING DEVICES (EWD)

Improvised early warning devices can be used to help secure any position you take for an extended period of time. They can be fabricated from a wide variety of materials and can be as simple as a long string tied to a bell or a pile of empty cans stacked in a hallway. You are limited only by your imagination.

Early warning devices should NOT be used in place of an alert team member on watch.

Early warning devices should be employed only on likely routes of approach. You can minimize their numbers by not using them in areas that do not allow for silent approach, such as thick brush or dry leaves.

Do not attempt to use EWDs as anti-Zombie weapons. Even under the most ideal circumstances, these devices will not reliably eliminate Zombies. They do, however,

EARLY WARNING

present a hazard to humans if positioned incorrectly. If the device employs ammunition or explosives, it should be pointed straight up or down. Also, remove projectiles and use only the primer.

EWDs that employ ammunition or other hazardous materials should have a reliable safety mechanism. The safety should always be engaged during transport and should be removed only when the device is set and the trip wire is in place. The safety should be designed so that it can be removed without having to place any part of the body over the device.

Make a sketch of the location of all devices to help ensure they are all retrieved. (Also add this information to range cards, if present.) Some simple devices that can be rigged with a minimum of time and effort are explained below.

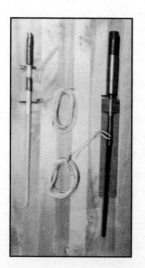

RUBBER BAND STRIKERS

The principle behind these devices is a tube with a rubber band-powered striker. A cotter pin acts as the safety; a nail acts as the trigger. The striker hits a small screw centered in the bore with turns of tape, which in turn impacts the primer of the cartridge. The device shown at left is made from a pen barrel, a chopstick, and a .357 mag. case (primer only, no powder or projectile). Make the device only as loud as necessary.

MOUSETRAPS

A mousetrap can easily be turned into a EWD. In this device, the spring-loaded arm of the trap strikes a shortened nail that is positioned to hit the primer of a shot shell. (The powder and shot have been removed for safety.) Make EWDs only as loud as necessary to avoid attracting Zombies from a distance. Ammunition that is damaged or otherwise not usable is ideal for converting into an EWD.

RATTLERS

This "rattler" was constructed in 20 minutes using materials found in a kitchen. The washer is from a light fixture, the arms are wire coat hangers, and the stake is a fragment of window molding. Two wound rubber bands spin the washer against the base of a soup can. A cork is used as a trigger. Aim the open end of the can toward your location to maximize the warning.

Zombies only have one goal:
to bite humans

Acronyms

BOO: Base of Operations
DZC: Daily Zombie Count
EWD: Early Warning Device
FSG: Familial Survival Group
GFO: Ground Floor Observer
LDD: Long Distance Distraction
LRM: Local Resource Mission
MKZ: Mutual Kill Zone
PMZ: Post Mortis Zombie
SSEA: Shotgun Shell Enhanced Arrow
VRV: Vrykolas-Romeros Virus
ZRO: Zombie Rights Organization

Terminology

Base camp: an area used to launch missions from
Breach: a gap in a wall, barrier, or defense made by a Zombie
Hot spots: areas of excessive resources that have a very high potential for Zombies or Zombie hordes
Lead-away: the act of intentionally leading Zombies away from other human survivors
Quarantine: a place of isolation in which survivors that have arrived from outside or who have been exposed to

Zombies can be placed for longer than two minutes to determine their safety

Rally point: a predetermined meeting area in case group members become separated during Zombie contact

Sign kit: a portable set of pre-made signs to be used on a mission

Staking: the act of destroying Zombie brain matter by piercing and gouging the Zombie through its eye sockets

Useful Slang

Blinded clean: a building with windows that have been successfully blinded without a breach

Ditching: getting rid of personal equipment or supplies to quickly lighten your load and allow you to run faster

Feeding frenzy: a Zombie that is engrossed in the eating of human flesh

Hive mind: the unification of purpose that occurs when Zombies form hordes

Mega-horde: hordes of 100 or more Zombies

Pool party: a Zombie eradication tactic that traps Zombies in fenced-in, outdoor pools.

Topping off: inserting ammunition into a gun's magazine (or "clip") when time allows.

eliminating Zombies is a service to your community

D2C   ZDAY 34   Sunrise 6:49am

TOTAL ZOMBIES : 4

–"Mr. Miller" still here, 3 days wandering
__PMZ__ aimlessly & babbling nonsense — sounds
like he's complaining but makes no sense.

–"Johnny" still stuck at neighbors. Been a __week__.
__PMZ__ It's official Zombies can remain stuck
at a door for a week.

?? new ZOMBIE. She looks about 11 years
old but not sure if she is post rigor
or not. She climbed into Cheryl's
car. Not sure why. light? Door is
wide open. Hope Cheryl's ok.

__NEW__ Evil Mailman is __FRESH__. He's standing
unmoving in the back yard.

Conclusion: LAY LOW..

Zombies don't dance

PRE-MISSION CHECKLIST

LAST-MINUTE CHECKLIST

- What is the temperature outside? Will it cause you to overheat?

- What time is the first and last light of day?

- Are all watches synchronized?

- Is there a prevailing wind? If so, which direction is it blowing?

- Does everyone have a kit?

- Do all team members know their role in the various movement techniques (e.g., bounding overwatch, column, or group)?

- Does everyone know what to do if an attack occurs?

- Are communication methods in place and clear to everyone on the mission?

- Are mission-critical supplies properly packed?

- If you are driving, did you pack a siphon hose, funnel, and gas containers? How about a blanket?

NOTES

NOTES